T0362696

a.k.a.
Fudgepuddle

Fin J. Ross

CLAN
DESTINE
PRESS

First published in Australia 2014
by Clan Destine Press

PO Box 121 Bittern
Victoria 3918 Australia

National Library of Australia Cataloguing-in-Publication entry

Ross, Fin J.

A.K.A. Fudgepuddle

ISBN   (pbk) 978-0-9923295-1-8

        (eBook) 978-0-9923295-2-5

Cover Design & Illustrations © Ashlea Bechaz

Design & Typesetting Clan Destine Press

Printed and bound in Australia by Five Senses

www.clandestinepress.com.au

For Steve

In memory of
Idgy & Taya

Morning is broken

It's just like any other morning. I'm snuggled into her armpit under the quilt enjoying that sort of semi-conscious reverie and feeling that vague quiver that indicates she might wake soon. It's always the happiest time for me, because I know that soon I'll share that quivering as her soft strokes at once arouse and soothe my senses. Starting from my head and working down my back it awakens my oogies and I can't control myself.

I start quirrelling and I turn up the intensity as I feel her body twitch and move sleepily. She presumes I do it for her pleasure, but that's just deuxjamb vanity. Deuxjambs recognise only a few of our feeliisms and they are haughty enough to believe we do it for their pleasure. Little do they realise that quirrelling is just a tiny part of a very complex language with which we communicate with our kisskies, our siblings, our parents, our friends and our rivals.

It's also how we reminisce, how we educate, how we settle differences, how we comfort... oh, and of course, how we manipulate those tall creatures on two jambs into doing what we want them to do.

Mind you, I have my deuxjamb well trained, but it took some time. For quite a while there she simply didn't understand what I wanted. She was forever picking me up when I had more important things to do, uncovering my secret hiding places just when I thought I had her really stumped, and putting all manner of ghastly-smelling things in front of me which I believe she actually expected me to eat.

My favourite pastime when I was a kisskie was to sit and quirrel angelically until she picked me up and then I'd turn myself inside out and perform a schpitzo. It even amazed *me* how many claws I could muster at once and how loud I could yarl while simultaneously biting into her hands and arms.

But what perhaps amazed me more was how ready she was to forgive me. Just half an hour later I could seek some fuzpah on her lap and she'd stroke me soothingly and apologise for being so bad to me. I'd curl my claws gently into her leg, just to remind her that I still had them and that they could be deployed into another schpitzo at an instant if the mood warranted it.

Through an in-depth but crash course in feeliisms, I'd taught my six kisskies how to perform mini-schpitzos at any appropriate moment – but only for deuxjambs, not among each other. I'd also taught them how to be pussano and quirrel a lot so that deuxjambs would find them irresistible.

But teaching them how to differentiate between nice deuxjambs and nasty deuxjambs took quite a bit of work. Most deuxjambs are so darn clever at disguising their real personalities.

I wish I'd had more time with my kisskies. How was I to know they'd be taken away to Weeras in a box or a carrier with unknown deuxjambs and I'd never see them again? That, of course, was a few months ago. Now I have no idea where Ori, Arni, Erna, Arelli, Inda and Sizi went. I just hope they're with loving and accommodating deuxjambs like mine.

Anyway, as I said earlier, I just love this time of morning

because I can reminisce in comfort until Hayoo puts her head under the quilt to say good morning in her dulcet whisper. It's such a pleasant moment. It's the time when I think she's most able to understand feeli-speak and so I reply in the special quirrel dialect I reserve for her.

Oh yes, she's rousing. I begin to stretch a little and turn up the quirrelling just as she's rolling over. And then–

'Jeeeeeeeeezus Christ!' she screams, and flings off the quilt in one move.

I leap two feet into the air and hover for a moment trying to decide which way to run. Every hair on my body stands erect as I contemplate a schpitzo, then realise that a spot of feelichatra might be better. In a split second I'm a quivering mess as far under the bed as I can get, just beyond the reach of Hayoo. I amaze myself with the speed at which I got here, since I'm usually a deft exponent of unvelocity.

'We're going to be late, Darling. Come on, get up, get up,' Hayoo screeches. Her feet hit the floor on one side of the bed and a moment later, Darling's feet appear on the other and he shuffles into his scuffs. They start running around in all directions. *And they say I can't make up my mind.* I just curl my claws into the carpet, keep quiet and wait for my fur to flatten again.

'Hayoo, we should've set the alarm for earlier,' Darling's voice booms from above the bed, 'then we wouldn't be running around like cut cats now.'

He plonks down on the bed and I have to crouch lower so the springs won't hit me on the head. I watch as he works his socks on and then his shoes.

They're obviously just late for work, again. I start to relax. It's just like every other morning. I crawl along on my belly and emerge from under the bed.

'Hey, Megsy girl,' Hayoo says, as she bends down to scratch me on the head, 'I suppose we'd better get you organised too'.

She bends down to pick me up and that's when I see the suitcase on the bed.

Me? Organised too? Oh no! The panic sets in. Time for a schpitzo. I try to back out from her grip, to go backward up over her shoulder. My claws sink into her shoulder blades. It's her screaming that does it. If she just didn't scream so loud it wouldn't freak me out so much. Somehow I get her hair caught in my claws and she screams more.

'Get her off me, get her off,' she shrieks. But before Darling gets anywhere near me I'm outta there. I make train tracks down her back and dive behind the chest of drawers where there's space on the windowsill to catch my breath and plan my next move. I feel the urge to sneeze 'cause it's so dusty and full of wobblycobs down here and I have to refocus my eyes to figure out what's tickling my nose. Humph, it's a daddy long– Actually, it's pretty small; it must be a baby longlegs. I eat it.

I realise it's a bit squeezier behind here than the last time. And don't go thinking it's because I've put on weight. I'm guessing that Hayoo has merely pushed the chest closer to the window the last time she cleaned down here which, by the look of it, was a long time ago. It's getting a little hard to breathe, especially with all these wobblycobs.

'I wonder why she did that. She never does that anymore,' Hayoo says querulously.

'I dunno, maybe she saw the suitcase.'

Yeah, like d'oh.

'Oh, don't be silly, she wouldn't know what that is. It's not like we go away that often. When was the last time – six or seven months ago?'

'I don't know, can't remember,' Darling replies.

I peer out from my hidey spot and it's then that I realise he's standing there with that horrid plastic basket in his hand. I stay put and contemplate my fate. There are two awful possibilities and neither fills me with pussano.

First: they're taking me to that place where we sit and wait and wait and wait. And I'm in my basket trying hard to look invisible, wishing I'd perfected the art of feelichatra, while all those snarly, bad-tempered quiffos sit around and drool and whimper and slobber. They've never learned the art of pussano and I'm sure not gonna be the one that offers classes.

And that's not the worst part. When the waiting's suddenly over, the real trauma begins: I get dragged kicking and screaming backward out of my basket while I scrabble for a claw-hold on the slippery plastic. I try the octopus trick in which I appear to grow four extra legs to make it even harder for them to extract me from the relative safety of my plastic haven. But what hope has a feeli got when it's three deuxjambs to one feeli – even an intelligent and resourceful one like me?

So I loosen my grip a bit and next thing I'm trying to get traction on that freezing, slippery slab, but my legs just go akimbo and I have to plonk myself in a most undignified fashion on the table. Oh the ignominy of it all. But I don't give in; hell, I never give in. It's just that sometimes, showing some fuzpah – even if it's just pretend fuzpah – can make the whole tawdry episode move along a little quicker.

But that does not mean that I in any way enjoy the prodding and poking and having that strange deuxjamb feeling me up, sticking things in my ooti, forcing my mouth open and checking out my tonsils and pearly whites. Not to mention staring into my eyes as though I'm gonna tell him something he doesn't know already – like why Catwoman only wears black.

I can't figure it all out, really. I get a tiny prick in the back of my neck and before I've even thought about feigning an impending schpitzo, I'm being bundled back into the plastic basket. Go figure. So I s'pose if I really think about it, the first scenario ain't so bad. At least it's usually over and done with pretty quick. But it's just dawned on me: Hayoo and Darling

9

wouldn't be packing suitcases, for themselves, if I were just going to Slippery Sam's.

That means – oh god, no – that means it's horror possibility number two: they're going away-away and they're gonna take me to... to La Cage aux Chats or worse – alCATraz. I try to peer around the corner of the chest to see how many cases they're packing. If it's two, I'm in real trouble. It could be weeks, months even. Darling turns to approach me and I try really hard to attain feelichatra; to just dissolve and disappear completely. But I suspect it's too late since he already knows I'm here.

The chest suddenly starts to move; I've got to think quick. I launch myself straight up in the air like a Harrier jump jet and manage to get a toe-hold on the top of the chest, figuring that a bit of catrobatics will enable me to fly over their heads onto the bed and from there to... well, anywhere out of reach.

But I hadn't figured on Darling being such a good catcher. It's all over red-rover when he snatches me right out of the air. Before I can deploy my tentacles he's got me into the plastic basket and he's shutting the door behind me. He puts the carrier down on the bed. I run rings around the inside, trying to get traction and I yarl as loud as I can. If they think I'm going to take this sitting down they've got another thing coming.

The panic starts to set in big time, and I realise my mouth is starting to go dry. Panting doesn't help, in fact it makes it worse. I'm getting all hyped, I tell you, and I reckon I'm about to indecorously let go a zilly. Actually – maybe that's not a bad idea...

'Oh, Darling can you smell that?' Hayoo asks.

'Yes, I can.' Darling's face appears right up close to the wire as he peers in. 'Oh Megsy, you haven't. Tell me you haven't piddled in there.'

'Meh?' I try to look adorable, putting on my best fuzpah face.

'Why do you do this *every* time?'

'Meh?'

'I'll get another towel, Darling, but you'll have to be careful not to let her out again.'

Now that's a thought. I wait for Hayoo to return. As Darling opens the door, I grab his finger in my teeth and, just as he pulls his hand away, I leap out without even touching the sides. In one move I'm out the bedroom door and skidding down the hall into the kitchen. My jambs slide out from under me but just as I'm about to hit the corner of the cabinet, I manage to get traction. Darling is gaining on me, but he too starts to skid.

I scuffle around in a circle and leap up on the bench and onto the yellum-box in two lightning moves. I skid and feel my back jambs starting to slide off the edge. I can't quite hold on – the top of the yellum-box is too slippery. But now I'm sort of all tangled up in this wiry stuff on the back of the yellum-box. I'm hanging there like the empty clothes Hayoo puts on the wire tree in the garden. I can hear a lot of grunting which I figure is Darling trying to work out what to do next. He puts his arm across the top of the yellum-box but can't quite reach me and then he disappears again. Then he comes back. Oddly, he's a bit taller now and he's looking straight into my eyes. I stare back. I lower my eyebrows and try to look mean.

'Can you see her, Darling?' Hayoo is obviously right beside Darling now.

'Yep, but I just can't grab her; she's fallen down behind. I might just be able to reach one paw,' he says, flailing his arms about.

'Well, we'll have to pull it out.'

Pull it out? Why would you want to pull my paw out? I shudder. Maybe this wasn't such a good idea after all. Next thing I know, the yellum-box starts moving in a sort of ziggy-zaggy motion and I'm hanging on for dear life. I can hear all sorts of funny noises coming from inside it. As it clears the wall beside me, I see Hayoo and leap off the back into her arms. She snuggles me up to her chin and I go all pussano; quirrelling loudly. I don't know why. It's not like I'm happy about this.

'You silly sausage, what did you do that for? Now, hop in here and calm down.'

Darling has the door of the carrier aimed at me and, after giving him an appropriately contemptuous look and an audible pfft, I oblige him by stepping in, turning around and plonking myself down. I guess I've just got to hike it or hump it.

The Lap of Luxury

So I'm in the back of the car, yarling a bit just to let them know I'm not a happy girl, but otherwise trying to keep a low profile. I'm dreading that any minute now the ticky tack is going to start and we'll slow down to turn onto that gravel road. The road to hell. I flatten myself out until my ears are lower than my chin. Any feelichatra expertise I might ever have had is deserting me.

But the car isn't slowing down, we're not stopping. I raise my head and just manage to see the sign out the window:

AlCATraz Boarding Cattery - 2km

It whizzes by and in an instant is out of view. Phew. But that means– *Eeek!* It's going to be La Cage aux Chats. I've never actually been there, but I heard some really bad things from some of the others at alCATraz last time. I mean, at least at alCATraz you've got enough room to turn around and you don't have to sleep right next to your own toilet. Hamish, that gorgeous grey I met at alCATraz last time, told me that he'd rather spend a week at Slippery Sam's than ever go back to La Cage aux Chats.

Hamish said 'cages' really *was* the right word for the tiny pens there, because the deuxjambs just want to cram more of us in like those chooks with batteries. It'd be like a human trying to eat, sleep and zilly all in a space the size of their rainroom. Hamish was very descriptive.

And, ooh, he was a honey. Those gorgeous green eyes and that fluurffy tail. Enough to make a usually sensible she-feeli swoon. We talked and talked for days. He had so many fascinating stories and he was genuinely interested in everything I said, even if my life seemed dull compared to his. I wonder what he's up – Holy hell! We're slowing down.

The ticky tack goes on. I don't dare to look. But I have to. I at least have to know in advance if I'm about to become a sardine. Once again, I stretch my neck up for a glimpse out the window. My heart's pounding ten to the dozen and I'm about ready to make another unpleasant mess in here. Then I see the sign.

The Lap of Luxury Holiday Park

Deluxe accommodation for your contented cat

Pphatt. Oh yeah? So let's see then. Nobody makes *me* contented against my will! Holiday park! What do they think this is – Disneyland or something? I suppose there are rides and fairy floss and a swimming pool. Like, sure.

We go up a long driveway with lots of trees. I can even hear some queekees over the sound of the engine. Darling stops the car. Next thing the door's being opened and I take a quick look around to see if there's any hope of a getaway, but before I know it I'm being carried up the path and over the threshold and the door clicks shut behind us.

'So who do we have here, then?' an unfamiliar, but not

intimidating, voice asks from behind the counter. I'm plonked onto the bench at eye level with the voice, which is coming from a pleasant-looking deuxjamb with long hair. I catch a glimpse of myself in her glasses and she smiles at me. Strangely, I feel relaxed. So maybe it's not the end of the world. Maybe this place will turn out to be better than either alCATraz or La Cage aux Chats.

'This is Megsy,' says Hayoo.

Uggh. Why must she call me that? How many times do I have to tell her my name is Juno?

'Oh yes, Megsy Campbell. Hello, girl,' the deuxjamb says, staring at me again. 'And who's a beautiful girl then?'

I'm starting to warm to her until she says: 'But you look like you could afford to lose a few pounds'.

Hey! I say what? I'm voluptuous, that's all. It's not like I eat too much or anything. I've just got heavy bones and I'm well insulated, thank you very much. Maybe my first impression of this deuxjamb was a bit generous.

Suddenly Hayoo's face appears over the top of the carrier. 'Bye Megsy, we'll see you on Thursday. You be a good girl now. Thanks Stephanie, I'm sure you'll take good care of her. You've been highly recommended.'

I give her a perfunctory snort. Wait a minute. Thursday, that's like, six days away. You mean I'm here for six whole days? I start to scream, just as I'm picked up and carried through one door and then another into a huge room. But my screams are soon drowned out by a cacophony of caterwauling.

Some smart-feeli from way down the back yells out at me: 'Don't forget, in a cattery, no one can hear you scream'.

Cripes, it's noisy in here. Too much noise for me to be able to think or to decipher who's saying what. There's a fire siren going off down the back, which is enough to make my hair curl and my claws straighten.

'This is your reception committee Megsy,' the deuxjamb says, 'they checking you out'.

I'm checking them out too as my hostess starts to parade down the centre of the large building. There's a veritable rogue's gallery of feelis, all lined up, one or sometimes two to a pen and they're all staring at me. She starts to reel off names, too quick for me to remember, so I make notes. The names will all be wrong anyway.

'First there's Lionel,' – *a tabby* – 'but you won't get much chance to meet him as he's going home shortly. Then there's Choux-Fleur,' – *not surprising, with those cauliflower ears –* 'and this is Blacky,' – *wow, that's original, for a black feeli.*

I spot two Siamese sitting side by side, very closely. Must be twins, I reckon. I'm almost past their pen when they introduce themselves. 'Hi, we're Thai and Tao, but our deuxjambs call us–'

'And this is Donald and Derek,' the deuxjamb says.

I crack up and they cringe. Why do deuxjambs give us such silly names? Why doesn't it occur to them to just ask us what we're called?

'Oh, and here's another Megsy. Look, she's a ginger like you, but she's going home tomorrow, so thankfully that will save me any confusion.'

What? Another Megsy? And *hang on*, she's nothing like me! She's wishy washy and long haired and I'm really more white than ginger, as you'll see that when I get out of this plastic handbag.

'And over there is Humbug,' – *a black and white, okay –* 'and beside him is Monty,' – *a big grey blob of a thing with a square face who, I swear to God, salutes as I'm passing.*

'Colonel Montgomery Enfield the Third', he says to me in a very regimented British accent.

'And you'll be in pen 23, right next to Zsa Zsa. Actually that's not her real name,' the deuxjamb whispers to me. 'Her real name's Belle, but I like to call her Zsa Zsa because she's quite the drama queen and thinks she's a bit special.'

The deuxjamb opens the pen and puts my carrier down on

the floor. I sit still for a minute. After all, I can't look too eager, can I? Maybe I'll just make her wait. I could try the schpitzo trick just so she knows who's boss, but I notice she's got bare arms and figure that mightn't be very nice. So I emerge slowly, sniffing the floor and looking all around what will be my abode for the next few days.

The first thing that impresses me is the space. There's plenty of it, and three or four different levels. I have a bit of a stretch then jump up onto a ramp and run up that and jump down onto a shelf. Wow, there's a really comfy-looking bed and two food bowls. But wait, there's more. I crawl back onto the ramp and jump up another level. There's another bed and a window. *Wow, I've got my own window?* My own view out over a garden. I can even see queekees in the tree. I'm thinking *Heaven*, maybe I've died and gone to Heaven. This is luxury all right. No wonder all the other feelis look so happy. Not like at alCATraz where everyone's ears are flat and there's barely enough room to stick their whiskers out.

Then the unthinkable happens. Deuxjamb leans across and opens the window! She points outside and gestures that I can go through if I want. I give her a squizzical. What? You mean I can go out there?

She nods at me as though she understands my hesitancy. 'Yes girl, you can go out whenever you like. At least until curfew, anyway.'

I see a sort of feeliwalk (and now I realise why it's called that) which leads to a three or four-level enclosure outside. It's even got a hammock. *A hammock!* I poke my head around the window and as I look along the outside of the building I can see three or four other feelis lounging around in *their* hammocks. I half expect to be offered a pina colada and sunglasses. Yep, okay, I'll confess, I'm pretty impressed: my own condominium. But of course I'll have to wait to get the lowdown on the place from the others, once this deuxjamb's gone.

I figure Hayoo must have come into some money to be able to afford this spiffy place and I try to avoid breaking into a quirrel. It's a bit soon for that. After all, I haven't even sampled the menu yet. I can't let on how impressed I am. I turn around and look into the deuxjamb's eyes. She smiles at me and reaches out to pat me on the head. I let her indulge herself momentarily and even raise my head a little to show her it's okay.

'You are a fatty, aren't you? I think a good diet and some exercise might be in order.'

Oh great, there she goes again, picking on my very special rotundness. I do what any self-respecting feeli would do when offended and lash out. I hook a claw into her cheek and she gives a short squeal and backs away.

Oops, I've drawn blood. I didn't actually mean to do that. It was her, she's the one who moved.

'Ooh you're a naughty girl, aren't you?'

What, you think I'm going to answer you?

'I think some nail clipping might be in order, too, but I guess there's plenty of time for that.'

Wow, I can't believe she's still smiling and she doesn't even seem to realise she's got blood running down her cheek. Now I feel rotten. Guilty even. I try to give her a sympathetic look but I suspect that to her I just look like I've got wind. She bends down to pick up my carrier and backs out the gate.

'I'll just leave you to settle in then, girl,' she says quite cheerfully. And off she goes.

I stay on the top shelf and survey my surroundings for a bit. I can't actually see all that much except for the pens across the way. Directly opposite I can see a svelte grey feeli pacing up and down. She does a sort of pirouette before each turn. I can't figure out if she's bored or if she's practicing something.

'Hey there, watcha doing?' I ask her affably. She takes a look at me and smiles but doesn't answer. Must be a snob I figure.

'She's Russian, silly, she doesn't speak English; at least not much,' says the fluffy black number in the pen next to her. 'She thinks she's a ballerina. At least that's what we think she thinks; either that or an acrobat or gymnast. Y'know these Russians are always athletic, serious and single-minded. She only came in last night and none of us has figured her out yet. Anyhow, I'm Maharani Shani, but my deuxjambs call me Taya. What's your name?'

'I'm Juno, but I get called Megsy.'

"Hmmph and they wonder why we don't come when they call us. I mean you couldn't ever confuse Megsy with Juno, or Taya with Maharani Shani.'

'That's for sure. So how long're you in for?'

'Just a week. I came in last night, too. But I've been here before so I know what to expect. It's pretty good, really. You been here before?'

'No. I've only been to alCATraz, which was really horrible compared to this.'

'Yeah, I've heard that. Hey Rocky, you've been to alCATraz haven't you?'

'Yeah,' says a deep throaty voice a few pens down. 'Terrible place, really terrible. Literally no room to swing a– well, you know.'

'Yeah I was there for a weekend once,' a squeaky voice pipes up. 'I spent the whole time with my head in my armpit just hoping and praying it'd be over soon. I gave my owners the real cold shoulder for a few days after that ordeal, so I think they must have got the hint. I just knew this place was going to be better the minute we came in the front door. I'm Roger by the way, I'm the teezee in 17.'

'Hi Roger. You're still pretty young, I'm guessing.'

'Yep, just four months old. And yeah I know my voice is still a bit squeaky, but yours would be too if you'd just had your notties cut off.'

'Oh you poor boy. Is it still sore?' I ask.

19

'Nah, I'm tough.'

'He's not really, you know,' whispers Maharani Shani. 'He cries himself to sleep at night'.

'I do not,' Roger splutters.

'You do too, lad,' says Rocky in his gravelly voice. 'But hey, that's what all wussy pussies do.'

'Don't be so mean,' an even deeper voice says. 'The poor lad's just homesick that's all. Even the best of us get homesick. Hi there Juno, I'm Daniel Coon.'

'But we all just call him Big Dan,' Rocky says. 'He's a Maine Coon you know, so of course being American means he's big, and I mean reeaal big. I thought *I* was big until I met Big Dan.'

I realise I'm having trouble hearing what they're saying because of the incessant siren blaring. 'What's with that really arrgarg siren?' I ask.

Maharani tips her head to the side as though she doesn't understand. 'Sire... oh siren. Ha ha. That's not a siren, that's Juniper. Hopefully she'll shut up soon. She goes off every time someone comes in. It *is* really arrgarg isn't it?'

I jump down from the shelf onto the ramp and then to the floor and, as I do so, I catch Maharani trying to stifle a giggle.

'What are you laughing at then?' I ask, eyeballing her.

She titters. 'You just looked so funny when you did that; what with all that flab flopping around, I thought you were going to trip over yourself.'

'Yeah, well you're no anorexic either.'

'Maybe, but at least my belly's not dragging on the floor. Boy do you need some exercise or something. You'd better join us girls after catnap hour then.'

'After catnap? Why what happens then?'

'You name it: catisthenics, aerobics, line dancing, singing, drama. Or Red and Mars sometimes run tai chi or tae kwon do classes. It just depends on the expertise of who's in here. You now, everyone has a talent to share,' Maharani answers.

'Who are Red and Mars?'

'Huh, oh sorry Thai and Tao I mean.'

'Why do you call them Red and Mars?'

Maharani looks across to the two Siamese and shrugs. 'Can I tell her guys?'

'If you have to, we know you will anyway,' they reply in unison.

'It comes from their breeder's names.'

'What's a breeder's name?'

'It's the name a breeder gives to pedigree kisskies and it's usually a real mouthful.'

'What's a *pedigree* kisskie? I haven't heard of those.'

I hear Big Dan clear his throat. 'Maybe I could explain that. A pedigree relates to a kisskie's ancatsors and whether they're good specimens of the specific characteristics of the breed.'

'Uh huh, so how do you find out about your pedigree? I'd *like* to know about mine.'

Maharani, Red, Mars and Rocky all crack up laughing.

'What, *what*?' I ask impatiently.

'You're not an ecsotique, so you don't *have* a pedigree,' Maharani says.

'How would you know?'

'Well d'oh, I don't really think that a big fat blobby white and ginger puddn's going to have any very special relatives hiding in her background. More likely your umbi just got knocked up by the neighbourhood boss feeli.'

'Now wait a minute, my umbi wasn't like that. She was always very particular.'

'She may well have been particular, but that doesn't mean you've got any pedigree blood in you. You're just a wuzzer, so you'd better learn to live with it,' Maharani says.

'So what about you, do you have a pedigree?'

Maharani puts her head down and looks sideways. 'Well it's not always so simple... '

'Don't avoid the question, I presume either you have or you haven't.'

'Mmm, I've got a part pedigree. My umbi's umbi was a pure-bred Persian but she... well she, shall we say, had a liaison with a, um, boss wuzzer feeli. And then *my* umbi well she sort of did too.'

'So you're a quarter Persian?' I chuckle. 'Well at least I'm a full-blooded wuzzer; not a quarter of something special.'

Maharani huffs and turns away, flicking her tail at me.

'You didn't tell me how Red and Mars got their names.'

'So ask them,' Maharani says huffily.

'Our pedigree names,' Thai says, 'and don't laugh, our names are Hazelvale Mongkut King of Siam Mr Red Tulip and Hazelvale Mongkut King of Siam Mr Mars Bar.'

'Ha ha ha,' I crack up, and flop on my side laughing out loud. 'What's with the chocolate bars?'

'Obviously, we're chocolate point Siamese, so we can only suppose our breeder thought it was funny.'

'It sure is,' I splutter. 'But then Red and Mars are a whole lot better than Donald and Derek'.

'If you think that's funny, you ought to hear Zsa Zsa's pedigree name,' Mars says, obviously trying to change the subject. 'Let's see, it's Superstarz Hollywood Honeybunch Prissy Miss Delilah. That's right isn't it, Zsa Zsa?'

There's a momentary pause and a well-rehearsed Jane Russell sort of voice replies, 'Yes, that is correct, Mars. And I do wish you'd call me Christobel. My parents were both highly awarded at all the shows.'

'Yeah, born on a bed of blue ribbons, that one,' Rocky pipes up.

'Oh, don't be so insolent and unpleasant, you old wuzzer. There's nothing wrong with being proud of your lineage. Besides, I'm going to be a queen when I get out of here.'

'Oh sure,' Maharani chimes in. 'I can just see the pageantry, Queen Zsa Zsa of... where?'

'Oh shoosh, you silly girl. I'm really going to be a queen. My deuxjambs have an extremely handsome ecsotique chinchilla lined up for me to… well, you know. So with my beauty genes and his strength genes, our kisskies will be just purrrrrfect. Like me.'

'Hmm. Modesty's a curse you know. So's humility by the way,' I say. 'I just bet none of them will be as much fun or as easy going as my kisskies, bless their hearts.'

'Yes, well I bet they were a mixed bag.'

'What do you mean?'

'I just figure that if you had kisskies they'd probably be every colour under the sun but without a hint of symmetry or style,' Zsa Zsa responds in her haughty voice.

'Individuals, yes, every one of them. And I taught them to be independent. I bet yours will be spoilt rotten by deuxjambs and completely unable to do anything for themselves.'

'I'm tiring of this conversation,' Zsa Zsa huffs. 'Besides, it's time for my morning nap. So let it be known that Queen Christobel is retiring to sleep.'

'Jeebs, what a performance. Anyone would think she's vying for an Acatemy Award,' I say, somewhat wittily I think. I hear Big Dan and the other boys chuckling.

'She does run the drama classes here,' Big Dan says. 'Apparently her umbi and fuddy are also sought-after actors.'

'Sure, and mine are champion athletes.'

Just then I notice a white feeli move to the front of the pen next to Maharani. I raise my paw and nod in his direction. 'Hi there, Juno's the name.'

'You're wasting your breath on him, he's deaf as a post,' Maharani advises.

'So what's his name?'

'Apparently his deuxjambs call him Snowy. Yeah, really original. But his name's actually Oscar. We all call him Beethoven though.'

'Why, coz he likes music?'

'No, silly. Because he's deaf.'

'Oh, I get it. Why's he got his ear to the floor?'

'He listens to the vibrations; he can tell when Miss Steph's coming way before any of us can hear her.'

'That's handy.'

'Yeah, it gives us a chance to stop what we're doing and put on our pussano faces so she won't suspect anything,' Maharani says.

'But what is it you do that you don't want her to know about? I mean apart from the exercise stuff.'

'Well, in the afternoons we have choir practice, bingo, reading group, music appreciation, ping pong, dizza, um, if it's warm enough we have luaus outside, or queekee spotting. It just depends on what we feel like doing. Or you can do nothing if you want. Some of the older ones just like to sleep all afternoon, but hey, that's up to them.'

'What's dizza?'

'Oh, that's a fun game. We'll show you later. Just make sure you don't eat all your kitzbitz, 'cos you'll need 'em for the game.'

What's in a name?

I wake up feeling a bit thick headed, like you do when you've enjoyed a really deep sleep and you're not really sure whether you're awake or whether you're still dreaming. I yawn and stretch my front legs out, spreading my claws. I roll onto my back and take a lazy glance out the window, with my legs still stretched out above my head. Nope, I wasn't dreaming. This is heaven on a fishstick, this place. I suddenly realise there's a lot of whispering going on around me. I prick my ears up.

'Shh, I think she's awake.'

'Must be, can't hear the snoring any more.'

Oh, oh, I have a terrible feeling they're talking about me.

'Could you possibly snore any louder?' Maharani asks.

'Who, me? I don't snore! I never snore.'

'Oh yes you do,' comes a number of voices in unison.

'We all had to put our heads under our blankets or armpits to drown you out during catnap hour,' Red and Mars remark.

'I definitely think you're a candidate for

aerobics, you need to get that heart pumping and get some air in those lungs. We'll be starting soon,' Maharani says with a flourish of her tail.

'So what are we waiting for?'

'The music of course. Miss Steph always turns the music on at two o'clock. But you might as well get down and start with some stretching exercises.'

'Oh, okay,' I say, reluctantly. I notice Maharani wriggling her chokeystrap up over her ears and onto her forehead. 'What on earth are you doing?'

'It keeps the fur out of my eyes, okay. I mean, you can't exercise properly with fur in your eyes,' she explains condescendingly, as though I should have known all about this gym club fashion faux pas.

'I've gotta say I've never really had that problem. You look like Olivia Newton John in *Let's Get Cynical*. Thank God you haven't got a leotard.'

I'm making my way down the ramp, I hear speakers – right over my head – crackle to life with the opening refrain of *Cool for Cats* which is, without a doubt, my absolutely favouristest song of all time. I look over and see Maharani putting her front paws up on the ramp.

'Here, watch me,' she says, 'I'll show you all the moves.'

I get myself into position and follow her lead. First we press our shoulders forward until our chest touches the ramp. We do that a few times. Then we turn around and spread our back legs and try to touch both sides of our pens with our front paws. That takes quiet a bit of effort for me and I know there's no way I'm going to reach.

Then she's got me standing on my hind legs stretching my whole body as high as it can go and next I'm on the floor doing puss-ups. This is getting pretty exhausting, I must say, and I feel like I'm about to break into a sweat.

'Hey, slow down a bit, will you?' I call out.

'What do you mean slow down? This is just the warm-up.'

'Cripes,' I pant. 'Well I think that's it for me. I'm gonna throw in the towel.'

'Oh, you're really puss-weak; you're never going to lose that flab if you don't put in the hard work. Don't tell me you're like Zsa Zsa and would rather pay someone to do your exercises for you.'

'Well it is all so unladylike,' says Zsa Zsa. 'And quite unbecoming to a feeli of my pedigree.'

'Hah, I s'pose you think your kackapod doesn't stink,' Rocky remarks.

'I am not even going to deign to answer that, you horrid wuzzer. It would be quite beneath my dignity.'

'Everything's beneath your dignity, Zsa. You've got that much stuff beneath you it's no wonder you sit up there so high and mighty,' Rocky says.

'Pfffft,' Zsa Zsa spits. 'And you only *think* you're tough because they put your tattoo on the *outside* of your ear. I bet you're really just all hiss and wind.' She scratches the carpety stuff on her ramp 'Oh, darn it, I've broken a nail.'

'Well I *am* tough, I'll show you all my scars to prove it,' Rocky protests.

'Young man, if you were so tough you wouldn't have any scars because you'd never come off second best. I bet Big Dan doesn't have any scars, do you?' Zsa Zsa says condescendingly.

'No madam, you're quite right, I have no scars and you have to look very closely to see my tattoo.'

I wish I could get to see Big Dan. His voice is enough to make me go weak at the knees; I'd love to know what he looks like. He sounds like such a gentlefeeli.

'When I was young, all the other kisskies in the street would goad and taunt me, trying to get me to fight, I guess because I was always so much bigger than them. I did box professionally for a while, but I found it all a bit pointless really, because I always won.

27

Sometimes I'd just give my look and they'd back off and wuss away with their tail between their legs. But I was quite famous there for a while. I still have some clippings from the *Cat 'o' Nine Tales Weekly.*'

'Wow,' Roger says, 'maybe you could teach me some basics. There's this absolute ratbag feeli next door at home who's always picking on me.'

'Well, I guess I could run classes, if anyone else is interested, eh Rocky?'

'I really doubt you could teach me anything. Like I said before, I'm tough.'

'I would be honoured to join your class,' the snobby-sounding British blue says. 'I never got to learn boxing while on active duty. That was something that was frowned upon by us officers, but secretly I always wanted to try it. Maybe I could be your enrolment officer, it would give me something to do.'

'Sure thing, if you'd like, Colonel,' Big Dan replies.

'Colonel Montgomery Enfield the Third at your service.'

'Shhh,' Maharani hisses, 'my favourite song's coming on.'

With that, Tom Cat Jones starts crooning, '*What's new pussycat? Whoa oo oh oo oh oh*'. Maharani starts singing along and I hear a few other voices chime in too, so I figure I might as well join in too. '*Pussycat, pussycat–*'

'Who on earth is that singing so flat?' comes a voice from a few pens down. 'If you're going to join in, please allow me to give you some private tuition first. We can't just have anyone piping in and spoiling it all.'

'Who's that?' I ask Maharani.

'Oh that's Finny, the singing teacher. You should listen to her, she's a beautiful singer. Voice like an angel. But then she's gorgeous to look at, too. She's a really pretty ragdoll. Some girls just have it all. Actually, I take that back; because there's one thing she can't do. She can't dance, she's just too floppy. You know, typical ragdoll. She lifts one leg and just falls over sideways. Completely and utterly uncoordinated. Her deuxjambs call her Sheba but Miss Steph calls her Bootiful.'

'So does Miss Steph have her own name for all of us?'

'Some of us, but I think it's only if she thinks you're special or if you're here long enough,' Maharani says.

'So what does she call you?'

'Princess, which I'm quite happy with really.'

'And what does she call Rocky?'

'Boofhead, or sometimes just Boof or Boofy,' Maharani says with a giggle.

'That's nearly as bad as Ralph, which is what my deuxjambs call me,' Rocky confesses.

'And before you ask, it was Miss Steph who first called me Zsa Zsa, and it's sort of stuck.'

'Oh, okay, so what does she call you, Big Dan?'

'Fess. She calls me Fess and I have no idea why.'

'Oh Big Dan,' says the Colonel, 'it's so obvious. Haven't you ever watched *Daniel Boone*?'

'What or who is Daniel Boone?' Big Dan asks.

The Colonel explains and I can almost hear the light globe going on over Big Dan's head. 'Huh, well I had no idea. That explains a lot. Oh yes, it explains a lot of the things she whispers in my ear.'

'Like what?'

'That's for me to know. But let's just say we have a bit of an understanding, Miss Steph and I.'

'Oh do you now,' says Rocky. 'Miss Steph and I have an understanding, too. She whispers to me too, you know.'

'And me,' says Maharani.

'What does she call you, Colonel?' I ask.

'Ahem. Monty Boy. Very unflattering for a feeli of my rank and social standing.'

'I'd take it as a compliment. She either thinks you're younger or cuter than you are.'

'I'd never thought of it that way.' The Colonel nods. 'Maybe you're right, young lady.'

'Jeez, I haven't been called that for a while.'

'So what does she call Beethoven and Roger and Blacky?'

'Beethoven she calls Snowman, and Roger she calls... Roger,' Maharani answers.

'Oh so she doesn't think you're special Rog?'

'She hasn't even got to know me yet. I've only been here a couple of days. But she calls Blacky, Possum, which is really not that far off because we call him Rabbit.'

'Why Rabbit?'

'Because when he runs, he always lifts both back paws at once, so he looks like he's hopping.'

'Oh,' I nod knowingly. 'Don't know how I'm going to remember all these names; it's all so confusing,' I confess.

'Don't worry darl, you'll get the hang of it in no time,' Big Dan says soothingly.

'Hey guys, isn't it time for drama class to start?' Roger asks excitedly.

I'm not sure I'm up for this so I meander back up the ramp and turn a few circles on the bed, prodding, clawing and pronkledonking it into shape. I plonk down. No, it's not quite right. I stand again and repeat the routine just to be sure.

Yep, that's better. I feel like I'm in a front row dress-circle seat in a fine theatre, just waiting for the show to begin.

'Now', says Zsa Zsa, 'we're up to the balcony scene, so Maharani you need to get up on the top shelf pronto and you need to look sort of innocent but sexy at the same time.'

'Yeah, I can do that. So where's Rocky?'

'He's down below in the courtyard sort of mincing around when he sees you appear.'

'Okay, I'm ready,' says Rocky.

'Okay, off you go then,' says Zsa Zsa.

Rocky clears his throat, paces to the front of his pen and adopts a statuesque stance. The he looks up in the air as though he sees something important. I can't imagine what. And then he speaks:

> *'But soft! What light through yonder window breaks?*
> *It is the east, and Juliet's in the sun–'*

'No, no Rocky, it's "Juliet *is* the sun" not Juliet's *in* the sun,' Zsa Zsa corrects.

'But how can a person be the sun? I don't get it. Where do they come up with this stuff?'

'Never mind, just keep going.'

'I would if you'd stop interrupting me. Where was I? Ah yes:

> *'Arise, fair sun, and kill the envious moon...'*

Rocky's voice puts me into a sort of sleepy daze and I struggle to keep my eyes open. I look across and see Maharani pacing along her shelf, waiting for her lead in.

> *'...And sails upon the bosom of the air.'*

Rocky cracks up: '*Bosom of the air* – how can the air have bosoms?'

'Oh Rocky, please try not to live up to my expectations of you. You've spoiled my scene, can't you ever just do it right?'

'Come on Maharani, just ignore him and keep going,' Zsa Zsa says.

'Okay, okay,' Maharani resumes her pose, and says"

> *'O Romeo, Romeo! wherefore art thou Romeo?*
> *Deny thy father, and refuse thy name:*
> *Or, if thou wilt not, be but sworn my love,*
> *And I'll no longer be a Catlet.'*

'Very good, Maharani, very good,' Zsa Zsa applauds.

Maharani flicks her tail and rubs her face up the wall as Rocky continues.

I've got to confess I've got no idea what they're going on about, nor can I figure out why she doesn't just jump down off the shelf and talk to him at eye level. But hey, I'm not going to interrupt.

I also can't figure out all the mewly-mewly. Why don't they just say what they want to say instead of beating around with a brush? And why on earth doesn't the girl want to be a catlet any more?

Beethoven's probably lucky he can't hear this; it's pretty yawny stuff. I glance across to his pen and see him with his ear to the ground.

A rascal called Raffles

'Shh, she's coming,' Beethoven calls out. 'Miss Steph is coming.'

He runs up his ramp to the top shelf and curls himself in a tight ball, feigning sleep. Maharani is quick to follow. I can't figure this out. When I arrived this morning everyone was up and screaming; now they're all pretending to be asleep.

'Psst Maharani,' I whisper 'how come we're all pretending to be asleep?'

'D'oh Juno, you know that all deuxjambs think we sleep all afternoon. We just like to live up to their illusions – you know, play along. That maintains the cattus quo. They think they're in charge and we go along with it so they think they've got us sorted out,' Maharani says.

'I see. That's clever. I mean, I do that at home but I didn't realise it was part of some grander scheme.'

'There's a bit of reverse psychology there too,' Big Dan whispers, 'because if we make them *think* we want to sleep all afternoon, they'll think we're being yawny and they'll go away and leave us alone, which gives us cat blanche to do whatever we want.'

I purse my lips and nod, my head tilted slightly. 'Makes perfect sense to me.'

I follow the others and curl myself into a pretzel shape. But I keep one eye open just enough to see what's going on. I see Miss Steph tiptoeing past, carrying a cage. Two green eyes the size of dinner plates peer out of a face, the likes of which I've never seen before. It looks like a cross between a spoffum and a hootle. Certainly I haven't seen a feeli that looks like that before.

'Here we are then, Raffles, number 25 for you. Now you settle in there and I'll be back in a tick with the camera, oh, and maybe I'll get a photo of Miss Fudgepuddle while I'm at it.'

Fudgepuddle! I crack up. Who does she call Fudgepuddle? What a scream. I roll on my back and try hard to stifle a big giggle just as she's walking past again, but I can't help accidentally letting out a raspberry.

'What's up with you then, girl?' She stops at my gate and peers in. I roll back over, give her a benign smile and put my head back under my armpit. I can't help wondering which poor sucker it is that she calls Fudgepuddle and I titter again. A few moments later I hear her coming back. I keep my head down and hear her footsteps pass by, followed by the click of a gate opening.

'It's okay boy,' she says soothingly. 'Now, smile for the camera, c'mon, stay still, no stay still. Oh c'mon, just for a second, will you? No, don't come towards me, just stay there. No, c'mon look at me, look at me. Ohh...'

She sounds exasperated so I guess this new boarder is giving her a hard time. Maybe he's camera shy. Not like me. I just love having my picture taken and I love all the gushy noises my deuxjambs make when they look at the pictures. They obviously think I'm some sort of screen goddess. I hear a click and then another.

'Good boy, Raffles, that should do me nicely,' Miss Steph says.

Which gets me to wondering. If deuxjambs think we don't understand what they say, how come they don't feel really stupid talking to us? They might as well be talking to themselves. I mean it's not like we're going to answer them. At least not in a language *they* understand.

I start to ponder about how misunderstood we feelis are. I mean, if TS Eliot had understood Mr Mistoffolees better, he'd have realised there was nothing 'magical' about him. He was just the master of feelichatra; which apparently just takes a lot of practice, not magic. But at least he acknowledged that we feelis all have our own name, which is ours to conjure up and ours to keep.

Really, not many deuxjambs do understand us. The Egyptians had it right. I mean it's obvious in the way they revered their feelis. After all, you don't see many quiffo mummies, do you? Yes, we were worshipped and adored just as some of us are today – if our deuxjambs have been properly trained. Emily Bronte, my favourite author 'cos she invented Catty and Heathcliff, knew what she was talking about when she wrote: 'A cat is an animal which has more human feelings than almost any other.'

And it's common knowledge that many well-regarded statesmen owe their greatness to their feelis. I mean Winston Churchill's feeli, Jock, actually directed most of the negotiations at wartime cabinet meetings. And Theodore Roosevelt's feeli, Slippers, made it his mission to ensure that guests to the White Home followed the right protocol. I know all this stuff 'cos I like to sit on the back of Hayoo's chair and read over her shoulder.

But when you think about it, it's obvious: we feelis only want to associate with good and kind deuxjambs. That's why Napoleon Bonaparte was terrified of us; because somehow *he* knew that *we knew* what he was up to. And we swore we'd tell everyone unless he was kind to us. We made him cross his heart and hope to die – that's why he always had his hand in his jacketfront.

I'm disturbed from my reverie by Miss Steph.

'Helllllooo Fudgepuddle,' she says as though introducing a quiz show contestant. My hair stands on end when I realise she's addressing *me* – and opening *my* gate.

'Whaaat,' I let out an agonising groan, or maybe it's a yarl. I can't quite tell. And then I'm drowned out by a dozen feelis all cacking themselves with laughter.

I'm mortified. And petrified – literally; I've turned to stone. I just sit like a statue with my mouth gaping. Miss Steph approaches me and raises the camera up to her eye.

'*In your bloody dreams*,' I spit. I snarl. I schpiff. I'm on the verge of a schpitzo and then I decide that a pfutt is a more appropriate gesture. So I huff, I turn around, I show her my back. I ignore her. Completely.

'C'mon Fudgepuddle, that's not very sociable.'

I continue to ignore her, stare at the corner and contemplate my next move. Burying my face in the pillow in ignominious shame feels like the most logical thing to do.

Fudgepuddle! Why me? Why Fudgepuddle? It's Juno, JUNO, don't you understand? I want to cry. And to think I thought she was nice.

'Okay, girl, I can see you're not ready for the camera yet. I'll come back when you're a bit more settled,' Miss Steph says. And then my whole spine shivers as she runs her hand down my back. If I were prepared to acknowledge it I'd have to admit it feels really good but I can't forget myself. I swish my tail from side to side and issue a low growl. She gets the hint and leaves me alone.

'Oh shut up you lot,' I schpiff when Miss Steph's gone.

'Fudgepuddle ha ha ha,' Maharani splurts. 'Fudgepuddle, Fudgepuddle...' she starts to sing and before long Rocky, Rabbit, Zsa Zsa and even the Colonel start to join in. I just want to shrivel up and die.

'What's so funny? Who's Fudgepuddle?' a tiny, cheeky voice asks. 'Hi everyone, I'm Riley. I'm the new one.'

'Hello Riley, I'm Maharani Shani, but you can just call me Maharani if you like. And I gather they call you Raffles, yes?'

'Yes that's right.'

'Why's that? Do you know? And, if you don't mind me asking, where did you come from? You don't look like any feeli I've ever seen. You're so tiny and you've got such big eyes. Actually you look like your umbi or fuddy was a ringtail spoffum or a slow loris. A-ha-he-hee,' Maharani titters.

'There's nothing slow about me. I'm a Singapura if you must know and I come from Singapore. Well *I* don't come from Singapore but my grandifeelis did. That's where we originated and that's why we look so ecsotique. No idea why they call me Raffles though.'

'Oh,' says Maharani. 'Anyway, you were asking about Fudgepuddle. Well, Juno over there, known by her deuxjambs as Megsy, has just been dubbed Fudgepuddle by Miss Steph… and, well,' she starts to chuckle, 'we think it's really funny but she's not too happy about it'.

'Ha ha ha, I wouldn't be either. Why, is she fat or something?'

'No I'm not fat,' I blurt out, 'I'm voluptuous. And voluptuous, for those of you who don't know, means sexy.'

'In whose thesaurus?' Maharani asks.

'Oh shut up. Shut up the lot of you,' I pout.

'Don't take offence, girl,' Big Dan croons, 'some of us do like a girl with a bit of meat on her bones'.

It's a pity I can't see Big Dan, because I'd love to know if his face matches his voice, which is just so dreamy.

'Thank you, Big Dan. At least someone has good taste around here.'

'Well actually, I'm a bit partial to a well-built girl too,' says the Colonel, 'I never could understand why the lads in my regiment got so besotted with all those bony bits of fluff, there's just no substance to them. No, I like a girl with plenty of flesh–'

'Stop drooling Colonel,' says Rocky, 'you're forgetting your good breeding.'

'Oh yes, yes, of course, excuse me, lad,' Monty apologises and changes the subject. 'So how long are you in here for, Raffles? And Raffles, for those of you who don't know, is known as the Father of Singapore. He was a British colonial official who founded Singapore. It's no shame to be named after him. So, just so long as you demonstrate the utmost integrity, I shall, from here on in, call you Raffles.'

'The 'father' of Singapore,' Raffles says in awe. 'I had no idea at all. And integrity is my middle name now, sir. I think I'm here for a couple of weeks. That should be long enough.'

'Long enough for what?'

'Long enough to escape.'

'But you've just got here, why on earth would you want to escape lad?'

'Why? Because I hate these places. They shove you in here and forget about you while they go off and see the world. It's not fair.'

'I should inform you, Raffles, that around here I'm the instigator and leader of the escape committee.'

'Oh, so what have you worked out?' Raffles asks cheekily.

'Well. I have worked out that these pens are impenetrable, so making an escape from inside here is impossible. The enclosures outside also are escape proof so that's out of the question and, ah… Miss Steph spends most of the morning in here, so that's no good. I think it would have to be a midnight run, but I'm still pondering the modus operandi.'

'So how long have you been here?'

'Two months.'

'Cripes! Two months and you haven't figured out anything yet. Glad I wasn't in a POW camp with you! You'd still be thinking about getting out six months after armistice was declared. Let me tell you in the last joint, they all called me Houdini, coz there's nothing I can't escape from,' Raffles boasts.

Something doesn't ring true to me. 'So how come you didn't escape from the last place you were in?' I ask.

'I did. I did! I got almost all the way home and then thought, d'oh, the deuxjambs aren't going to be there to feed me, so what's the point.'

'So what did you do? Did you go back?'

'Hell no. Why would I go back when I was so desperate to get out of there? Actually, and I'm a bit embarrassed to say so, but while I was sitting on the side of the road just minding my own business and thinking about what to do, up rolls a deuxjamb all dressed in green, grabs me in a net, shoves me in a cage and carts me off to the AFAQS. And if I'd thought AlCATraz was bad, well the AFAQS was worse. I'm shoved into this tiny little dark cage, barely enough room to turn around and I'm surrounded by all these feral feelis who'd sooner spit at you than give you the nod.'

'Ohh, so you were in AlCATraz too? We were talking about that before, it sounds terrible,' Maharani says.

'Yes, just awful,' Raffles agrees, 'but, as I said, not as bad as the AFAQS'.

I confess I'm a bit bewildered. 'What's the AFAQS?'

'D'oh, it's the Abandoned Feelis and Quiffos Shelter of course.'

'Oh, of course,' I nod like I should have known that.

Zsa Zsa pipes up. 'So what happened then?'

'Well I was there for a day or two and I'd just figured out how to blow the joint. I had it all planned, when suddenly my deuxjambs turn up and bail me out.'

'But how did they know you were there?' I ask.

'I dunno. Maybe it was the device that was secretly implanted in my neck a couple of years ago. They thought I didn't know it was there,

39

but I knew I wasn't paranoid when the greencoats waved their telephone over me and it beeped. Clearly my deuxjambs like to keep track of my movements.'

'Hmm, you're not the first feeli I've come across who thinks they've had something implanted? This sounds like a conspiracy to me,' the Colonel says in a low thoughtful voice.

'Anyway, the one good thing is that at least my deuxjambs know that AlCATraz isn't escape proof. So I guess that's why they've brought me here this time,' Raffles says. 'But I'm sure I'll be able to figure out a way out in a day or two.'

Suddenly Rabbit interrupts. 'Psst – okay whose deuxjambs drive a dark blue sedan?' he calls out.

'Not mine. Not mine. Mine neither,' a chorus of voices rings out.

'Oh, oh must be someone coming to look then. Okay everyone, assume pussano positions, quick,' Rabbit advises.

'What's happening?' I ask. I obviously still have some protocol to learn.

'Just sit and look happy and appealing because if they like the joint, we might get to meet someone new before long,' Rocky whispers.

'Oh, okay,' I say obligingly as I wander back up the ramp and start pronkledonking my bed.

'Maybe, when they're gone, we can get back to our drama lesson,' Zsa Zsa says.

'Nah, it must be about time for tai chi, isn't it, Mars?' Rocky asks.

'Yes, we could if you like,' Mars replies.

I get to thinking about our earlier conversation and how Maharani said that everyone has a talent to share. My mind starts to race. Talent?

I could um… no, maybe… nah, they'd just laugh, um… oh I know, I could… no. Oh cripes. I don't have a talent, there's nothing I do well. Except eat, maybe. I could teach them how to scoff your food so quick that you always get a second helping. No, maybe not. They'd just make fun of me.

I start to panic. What if they ask me what I'm gonna teach? What'll I do? Do I just admit that I don't have any talent? I start to break out in a sweat. I lick my paw and wipe behind my ear, more to make myself look busy than from any sense of vanity.

I hear footsteps and Miss Steph's now-familiar voice.

'Oh yes, it's very comfortable, and as you can see they're all very happy,' she explains as they approach Zsa Zsa's cage.

'Oh look darling, isn't she a beautiful girl, so elegant and self-assured,' a male deuxjamb says.

'Oh yes, she's not unlike our girl,' says the female deuxjamb. They linger a bit longer in front of Zsa Zsa's gate and then glance in at me.

'Oh look, what a fatty,' the strange she-deuxjamb squeals.

'Yes, she is,' says Miss Steph. 'She just came in this morning so I'm still getting to know her. Her name's Megsy, but I'm going to call her Fudgepuddle, because that's just what she looks like: a big puddle of fudge.'

Oh the ignominy of it all.

I turn to face them, plonk myself down, raise one leg and start licking my ooti. That's about what I think of them. They seem to get the message and keep going.

The talented Miss Fudgepuddle

As I'm sitting here taking in my surroundings, I start to feel sorry for the Russian Blue opposite. Nobody talks to her and she just keeps pacing and flinging herself around her pen. I still want to know what it is she's doing. I stand up and have a good stretch, arching my back like the Harbour Bridge and then saunter down the ramp and jump to the floor.

'Hey. Psst,' I try to attract her attention. I wave my arms around and stretch up and rattle the gate. She finally stops pacing and looks over at me.

'Nadia Comaneci?' I say. She shakes her head. Hmm, so obviously not a gymnast. 'Katarina Witt?'

'Nyet,' she replies.

'Hmm, so not an ice skater either.' I ponder a moment. 'Anna Pavlova?'

Her head flings up and a smile beams across her face as she nods. 'Da, da, Pavlova,' she nods animatedly and bats her paws together.

'Ah. So like Swan Lake, Nutcracker, Tchaikovsky?'

She starts to get really excited now and it seems I've found a way to communicate with her. She performs some snazzy move like an arabesque or pirouette or whatever you call it and finishes with her tail high in the air. I give her a clap and she curtsies for me.

'Spaseebo balshoye,' she says. I look at her quizzically. 'Spaseebo balshoye,' she repeats.

'Oh, I get it, you're with the Bolshoi Ballet.' I'm quite proud of myself for figuring that out. But my pride is short lived.

'I think you'll find, Juno,' the Colonel says, in what promises to be a patronising correction, 'that she's saying thankyou very much. I believe balshoye means very much.'

'Oh.'

'Vy gavareeteh pa ru-sky?' She asks, but I realise she's addressing the Colonel not me.

'Nyet. Pozhaluista. Ya ploha gavaru pa Ruski,' the Colonel answers.

I'm impressed, but then I remember his military background. Maybe he was a spy, a double agent even. But he quickly shatters my illusions.

'Sorry, but that's as much Russian as I know: *no, please,* and *my Russian is bad,*' the Colonel confesses.

The grey sits there looking confused and expectant like she wants to talk some more. I squint up at the card on her pen and can just make out her name.

'Leonora?' She nods excitedly, so I point to my chest and introduce myself. 'Juno,' and I point to her 'Leonora'. She nods and points to herself, 'Lara', and then points to me 'Fu...udgepuddle?'

'No, nyet; don't call me that, please don't call me that. It's *Juno,*' I emphasise. She nods and smiles in agreement.

'Hello Lara, I'm Christobel, but you can call me Zsa Zsa.' Lara nods and repeats 'Zsa Zsa; da Zsa Zsa.' Lara performs another curtsy-thing and indicates to us to copy.

'I think she's trying to give us a lesson, Zsa Zsa.'

'It would seem so,' Zsa Zsa replies.

I attempt to copy Lara's move and find myself off balance and flopping onto my side. Lara titters at me. Obviously comedy is comedy in any language. But I could have told her that ballet's really not my thing. I mean, you've got to be skinny but strong at the same time for that and something tells me I'm never gonna fit into either of those categories.

Oh oh, back to talent again. I've just gotta hope I'll get through my time here without anyone asking, otherwise I'm really gonna be a laughing stock. I don't know, I've just never had it in me to be bothered learning anything.

'I think I'm getting the hang of this,' Zsa Zsa comments, 'it's a bit tricky though because there really isn't enough room in here'. Suddenly I hear a bang on the other side of the wall right beside me. 'Oh darn, I've broken a nail.'

Now I'm aware of rustling and scratching noises; it sounds like someone having an argument with a newspaper.

'What's going on?' I ask.

'Rocky is making sure he gets noticed,' Zsa Zsa says.

'Gets noticed by whom?'

'By Miss Steph of course.'

'But what's he doing and why does he want to be noticed?'

'He seems to figure that if he makes a real mess with his kackapod, spreading it all over the place, that she'll spend more time in there with him and pay more attention to him,' Zsa Zsa explains.

'Sort of a negative move for a positive result isn't it?'

'Yeah, but so far it seems to work. She'll be in there for 15 or 20 minutes every morning berating him for being such a grot, but all the while she's patting him, stroking him, dopping heads and all.'

That's not so stupid then, I figure. Maybe I should try that myself. Besides, I haven't even checked out *my* kackapod yet.

I amble to the back of the pen and step into the blue plastic tray. I shuffle around in the grey pellets and then notice the white paper lining the bottom. Without being too obvious that I'm copying Rocky's idea, I start to fiddle with it, quietly.

I paw the pellets into one corner and then get my paw under another corner and lift it up, stepping onto the overlap to make a fold. Then I lift the other corner and quietly fold that too. I slide my back foot forward and curl a section of the paper up and sort of flop on it and then with my left elbow I scrunch the paper a bit. I get a folded bit between my front paws and stand up on my hind legs and bat it and fold it again, sort of like I'm trying to catch a flupperty but with my feet still on the other end of the paper. I stomp on the bit still in the kackapod and make a twisty movement as I fold it over the edge.

Then I accidentally put my foot on the side of the tray and it tips up, sending me unceremoniously onto my face with my ooti in the air. The tray flops back again but half the pellets are spread all over the floor and the paper wafts to the front of my pen.

'What *are* you doing?' Maharani asks.

'Huh?' I respond while trying to compose myself. 'Just playing, that's all.'

'So what's with the wimby?'

'Wimby? What wimby?'

'The paper wimby you just made,' she says pointing beside me.

I look at the mess I've just made and still can't figure out what she's going on about. 'What do you mean?' I ask blankly.

'You've just turned that bit of paper into a perfect wimby, from this angle it looks like maybe a salmon or trout.'

I change my position a bit so I'm looking from the same angle. She's right; it does look like a wimby, just like a much bigger version of the ones that swim around in the big glass at home. I shrug.

'That's really very clever,' Maharani says. 'You actually made something out of paper. I've only ever seen that sort of thing once before; but where? What is it?

'Oh, I know what it is,' she says, pointing at my wimby in excitement. 'It's, um, okinawa, no, organza, um no, salami; no, what do they call it? You know, the Japanese thing when they fold up paper. You should know Red or Mars.'

'We should remind you, Maharani, that we're Siamese, not Japanese, and there's a big, big difference,' Red and Mars say.

'Yeah, yeah, sorry. But don't you know what I mean?'

'Origami, we do believe.'

'Yes, yes, that's it. You should see what Juno's made. She's so clever. It's a really neat wimby; it looks just like a real one, and she just whipped it up out of her kackapod paper. It didn't take long, did it Juno? I'd love to learn how to do that, will you show me how?'

I start to puff my chest out and make a sweeping gesture with my head, sort of like a bow. So, I've made a wimby out of kackapod paper! Maybe I've got a talent after all. Quite accidentally.

But, uh-oh, can I do it again, let alone show someone else how to do it? Doubtful, and now I can't even try another one 'cos I haven't got any more paper.

'I've never given instructions before, Maharani,' I say, as if that's the only problem I have. 'But we can try. Grab your paper and I'll see if I can teach you how.'

I just hope to hell I can recall some of the moves and folds.

'I can't now, my paper's all wet. I'll have to wait until Miss Steph gives me another kackapod.'

'Oh, foop,' I say. Just when I'm all enthusiastic about something. Typical.

'We shouldn't have to wait too long; she'll be in with dinner soon,' Maharani says. I lick my lips at the mention of food.

'So what do we get for dinner?'

'Hmm, could be tinned delicacies, or mince, or queekee-fowl. What day is it?'

'Friday, Maharani.'

'Tuna-wimby then, it's tuna night. My favourite.'

Now I'm really starting to salivate. I flick my tongue out to collect the drool. Maybe if Miss Steph sees my masterpiece, she'll give me a second helping. *Tit for tat, Tuna for Juno, give me some more, I'll be over the moono*, I sing in my head. This place keeps getting better.

I just wish there was more paper around though. I'm keen to see if I can make something else. I'm still thinking that thought when something hits me lightly on the head.

I look down and see what looks like a paper floomee. I look all around trying to figure where it's come from.

'Did you get that Fudgie?' It's Raffles' squeaky voice.

'Yes thanks, right on the head. How did you–'

'My fuddy taught me. I make them at home all the time. Just a tip though, the paper the deuxjambs use in their kackapod room isn't any good. It's too floppy. You need nice crisp paper like this or they won't hold their shape. I had to aim that pretty carefully too to get it through the wire.'

I pick up the floomee and flick it through the wire in the gate. It flies gracefully across the aisle and straight into Lara's pen. She in turn picks it up, studies it for a moment and throws it towards Zsa Zsa. Before long it has made its way to the Colonel after a zigzag flight path with several landings and take-offs. I hear some rustling.

'I think a couple of minor modifications here, just tipping the nose down and altering the tail a bit, will make this fly all the better, young Raffles.'

I can't see what the Colonel's doing from here, but it sounds like he knows what he's talking about.

Well, at least I thought he did.

'Oops,' he says, 'looks like I might have overdone it.'

'What're we gonna do now?' Rabbit asks. 'I can't reach it. What about you Humbug, can you reach?'

I push my face right up to the wire of my gate and try to peer sideways down the building. I can just see a black and white paw sticking out of a pen further down and opposite. He's through the wire up to his armpit but he still can't reach the floomee. His face is also squashed into the wire, making him look really weird.

'Nah, can't get it, Colonel. What are we gonna do? Miss Steph's gonna be here any minute,' Humbug says.

'I don't know. Just try to look innocent, nonchalant, when she comes in. Maybe she'll think those deuxjambs dropped it,' the Colonel advises.

'That's silly, Colonel. How many deuxjambs do *you* know that walk around with paper floomees in their pockets,' Humbug says sarcatically.

'You may be right. But don't you think she'll think it's more obvious than the alternative?'

'Huh? Oh, yeah I guess so. Tell me how to look nonchalant.'

'Pussano, Humbug; just try a bit of pussano instead.'

Meanwhile, I take another look at my origami wimby and fiddle a bit to improve the fins.

'Hey you had better do something in your kackapod, or she mightn't change it,' Maharani suggests.

'Oh yeah,' I agree. I pace to the tray and scratch around a bit before squatting. 'Do you mind not watching?'

'Oh, sure,' says Maharani turning 'it's not like I haven't got better things to do'.

With that, Beethoven suddenly gives the signal so I quickly cover my zilly with some pellets and make my way up to the top shelf to assume pussano position. But...

My attention is totally diverted by a tiny queekee perched in the wire of my condo. I drop to a crouch and pop my head out the window. I'll sneak up on it. I flop into the feeliwalk. It doesn't even move. It just sits there, staring at me. Either it's blind, stupid or very quick. I stretch a paw out and still it doesn't move.

I surreptitiously slide along the feeliwalk, rolling onto my side as I go but never taking my eyes off it. I slowly raise my paw up behind my head. I'm virtually within striking distance. I'm like a stealth bomber zeroing in on its target. But I'm stuck; suddenly I can't move. My claw's stuck in the carpety stuff and the bloody queekee's still sitting there. It just looks at me and chirps.

Why do these things keep happening to me?

Humph, can't be bothered anyway. Why exert myself when there's tuna for dinner?

'What are you doing, Fudgepuddle?'

I nearly jump out of my skin, which at least has the desired effect of freeing my claw. I didn't even hear her sneaking up behind me.

'What a mess, what have you been doing?' Miss Steph says as she approaches. I try to see past her to nod at the floor to show off my masterpiece. I think she'll be pretty impressed; it might even be worth a second helping of dinner.

She moves aside a little and I see a flattened, squashed wimby. It's dead; she's stepped on it. I let out an audible tut and shake my head.

'Whatsa matter girl?' she asks.

What do you bloody think? I put all that effort in and you've just gone and stepped on it; squashed the life out of it.

'What a mess mucker,' she says, just to rub it in. She bends down and grabs the paper, scrunching it into a tight ball. I look over her shoulder at Maharani and Lara who are both shaking their heads in disgust.

'So much for that,' I call out.

'Yes, what a shame,' Maharani replies.

Miss Steph backs out the gate. 'Okay, dustpan, new litter tray and dinner,' she says as she heads off down the room. 'What's this then? Huh, that's odd.'

I hear Humbug and the Colonel and some of the others tittering. She returns before long, by which time I'm sitting on the top of the ramp.

'Here girl, how about some tuna – real tuna, *human* tuna, not that crappy stuff from a cat food tin.'

I lick my lips to show her I understand and she places the plate on the bottom shelf. I dop her head which seems to surprise her. All is forgiven if this tuna is as good as she says. She dops me back and tickles me under the chin. I turn on a momentary quirrel and drop down onto the shelf.

Wow, it sure smells good. I lick some juice and then tentatively sample some of the pink flaky stuff. Yuuum! I hoe in, quirrelling at a deafening volume at the same time. There! Gone! More please. I look up at her with my best pussano expression and quirrel a little louder.

'What a garbage guts,' she laughs. 'I s'pose you want a second helping.'

Yes please, pussy please. I know she can read my mind. I just get the feeling that this deuxjamb is pretty intuitive.

'I'm sorry girl, but your mother and I discussed a special diet for you, which unfortunately means no second helpings. So you're going to have to learn to savour your food. Eat it slowly and make it last.'

'Oh foop!'

'I could have been a cattender'

I start to wonder what's taking Miss Steph so long. After all she's already fed us all, so why doesn't she buzz off so we can get on with our game? I can hear her down the other end of the room and there seems to be lots of quirrelling going on – I can feel the fuzpah from here.

'Hey, what's going on?' I call out to anyone who might be listening.

'Oh, we're just getting our goodnights,' Humbug calls back.

'What's that?'

'Well, after she's fed us all – and before she goes – she gives everyone a cuddle and tucks us in.'

'Oh. Sounds good to me.' After what seems like an eternity, Miss Steph finally gets back to my quarters.

'Now, Miss Fudgepuddle, time for a quick cuddle before I go.' She's still speaking as she picks me up and holds me close to her chest and squeezes me in a very satisfying way. I can't help but quirrel – she really knows how to push my fuzpah button. She rubs her forehead on mine and blows hot breath in my ears. I turn to mush.

She leaves me there and progresses all the way down, giving everyone else a cuddle along the way until she finally gets to the door. As she turns the lights out she says: 'Goodnight, you prints in the main, you kinky new winglets'.

'Huh?' I ask, 'what did she say?'

'Not really sure,' Zsa Zsa says, 'but she says it every night'.

I'm sitting in my kackapod trying to get the inspiration for another creation when something hits me on the head and bounces off onto the floor. It's a kitzbitz. A slobbered-on kitzbitz.

'What the–'

'Are you going to join in, Juno? Maharani asks. 'We're having a game of dizza. I hope you remembered not to eat all your kitzbitz.'

'Sure, so long as you tell me the rules and it doesn't involve me getting pelted with your soggy breakfast.'

'Okay. You put a kitzbitz in your mouth, but don't chew it, right; then you spit it as far as you can. Now, you can aim into Lara's, mine or Beethoven's pen. If you get it through the wire into one of our pens it's worth five points, if you get it into one of our kackapods it's worth ten. But, of course, we can try to stop it coming in. If we block it or it doesn't get this far you get no points. Get it? We start when the bell rings.'

'What bell?'

'This one.' Maharani points to her collar.

'Sounds simple enough. But what's actually the point – I mean what does the winner get? It seems to me that the loser would be better off; they could just eat all the kitzbitz they can collect.'

'Oh yuck. Trust you to be such a glutton. Would you really eat something someone else has slobbered all over?'

'Huh? Yeah, if I were hungry enough.'

'We just play for championship points. Big Dan is the current champion. Coz he's so big, he can spit a way long way; and he'll sometimes spit two or three at once,' Maharani says. I begin to feel relieved I'm not opposite Big Dan's pen.

Whoa! I have to duck quickly to avoid one of Beethoven's kitzbitz flying at me.

'Hey, Beethoven, we haven't even started yet,' I call out.

'Yeah but *he* doesn't know that,' Maharani says. 'Okay are you ready everyone?'

'Yes, okay, I'm ready, go for it,' come the responses.

Suddenly it's like all-out war. Before I can even load up a kitbitz I'm being pelted centre, right and left. How come all three of them are picking on me?

I quickly load my mouth with three or four kitzbitz and spurt. Three hit the wire and flick back at me and the fourth rolls into the middle of no-feeli-land.

I've got to get the knack, and quick. Maybe just one at a time is the idea. I try that, aiming directly across at Maharani. I spit and… Bugger, it hits her gate and bounces back. I load again and spit. Yeah, yeah, it's looking promising…

No. She sees it coming and blocks it with her shoulder and it flips back out. It's not as easy as it sounds, this game.

I try again, but the next one lands in the potplant between Maharani and Lara's pens. I should mention that all the while I'm getting clobbered. I feel like one of those poor queekees in a shooting gallery. There's just no way to get out of the way. Surely they must be nearly out of ammunition.

I look in my bowl and there's only two kitzbitz left. I pick up one and spit it directly at Maharani. My timing's perfect, coz while she's ducking to avoid one from Zsa Zsa, mine sails through her wire, over her head and into her kackapod. Yeah, skilling shot!

I pick up the last one from my bowl and aim it at Beethoven. It's a more acute angle, so it's going to be a bit awkward. I spit and it goes clear through his wire and hits him on the rump as he's turning.

Yes!! I wave my paw in an arc of self-congratulatory praise. But it's not my last, of course, because my pen's full of everybody else's kitzbitz and they've all got none left.

So here's my dilemma. Do I keep the game going or do I keep my kitzbitz for a midnight snack?

I'm still contemplating this when I hear a rattle nearby and I see Maharani's head turn quicker than a courtside fan at Wimbledon. She lets out an astonished yarl.

Whaaat?

Then my eyes nearly fall out of my head, as a tiny face suddenly appears at my gate.

'Hi Fudgie. It's me – Riley.'

'Riley? Raffles! H'how did you get out?' My jaw is somewhere down around my elbows.

'Easy peasy. I told you they call me Houdini.' He starts to climb my gate and, as he gets halfway up, he flicks the catch across and the door starts to swing open – with him still attached.

'Weeeee,' he squeals, like he's on a fairground ride.

I'm just so moosh-thwacked I sit there as though my moosh has been thwacked. Raffles jumps down and darts across to Maharani's pen. Within about three seconds her gate is swinging open too and, as it swings out on its arc, Raffles reaches out and unlocks Beethoven's pen with his free paw.

'Who wants to party then?' he squeals.

We're all still sitting inside our pens, rigid with disbelief.

'Well I never,' Zsa Zsa says matter-of-factly.

Maharani delicately stretches her paw across the threshold as though she's testing the bath water. She takes one cautious step, her rump and tail low to the ground. She peers around and nods.

'It looks okay. The coast's clear,' she says, stating the obvious.

So I follow suit, stretching my front legs and sticking my ooti in the air and yawning as though this sort of prison break happens every day. I start to stroll down the aisle, getting a good look for the first time at Zsa Zsa, Rocky and the Colonel. The Colonel looks like he's just seen a Gorgon. Raffles is ahead of me, darting back and forth opening all the gates.

'Raffles, young fellow,' says the Colonel in an authoritative voice, 'I must advise that you have flown in the face of the correct protocol here. Any escape plan is to be submitted to the escape committee, of which, I should remind you, I am the officer in charge. It must be voted upon and planned in every detail. Imagine the confusion if everybody just takes it upon themselves to break out when they please.'

'Yeah grandfuddy, whatever,' Raffles says, brushing aside the Colonel's imperious superiority with a cheeky flick of his tail.

Suddenly I'm confronted with a towering presence; a gorgeous hunk of a feeli with dreamy eyes, a mane like a lion and ears like a lynx.

Oooh… I start to wobble like a bowl of blancmange and I'm sure my eyes are rolling in my head. *So* not what I was planning for a good first impression. I wanted to look svelte and sexy. Instead I look like a beached wobblygong on speed.

'And you must be Fudgepuddle, er, sorry, Juno,' he says looking at me with intelligent eyes.

'Mmm,' is all I'm capable of responding. He's definitely as handsome as he sounds and I'm a veritable bowl of mush, a puddle of fudge… Oh cripes, a fudgepuddle even.

'Brrrr,' my comment reverberates as I vibrate my lips.

'Is something the matter?' he asks with sincere concern, his right eye closing like a slow, seductive wink.

'No, no not a problem,' I blubber. 'I'm, I'm just stunned at being out I think,' I lie. I rub my chin up the side of Big Dan's gate for his later appreciation.

'Yes, it's remarkable isn't it? Fancy it being so easy to get out of our pens. Obviously it takes a smart, tricky youngster like Raffles to achieve the impossible. Isn't that right, Colonel?' Big Dan smirks a little as he says it, not really expecting a reply from the old boy.

'By jove, I think I must be ready for retirement. To be outsmarted by such a young snipper-waffer,' the Colonel concedes. He's the only one who hasn't emerged from his pen yet. I take a couple of steps backward and see him still sitting up on his shelf, a supercilious expression on his boofy grey face.

'So are you coming out, Colonel?' I invite.

'No, I'm not in any hurry to be going anywhere. At least not according to anybody else's agenda,' he says with a superior air as though he has a mouth full of woozel. He puts his paws out in front of him and adopts a sphinx pose; his face a cross between uppity superiority and feigned ennui.

'So what do we do now?' Humbug asks as everyone mills around and sniffs each other's ootis.

You really have to hope you've cleaned there properly when a complete stranger wants to check you out. But it's a great way of finding out what neighbourhood someone's come from, whether they're an ecsotique or a wuzzer and, of course, what they had for breakfast.

There's a couple of feelis I haven't even met yet, so I introduce myself. There's Lionel, a cranky-looking old teezee. Then there's a very haughty-looking, boring as batgrunty, black bloke called Professor Faraday who just ignores me. He seems bent on ignoring everybody else too. So I decide to make it my business to ignore him.

I notice Red and Mars sticking together like glue and wonder how they'd cope if they were ever separated. They walk as though they're joined at the hip and I get the impression one always knows what the other one's thinking.

Suddenly happy hour is interrupted by loud mezzing and the crowd parts to reveal Rocky and Humbug facing each other off. Their backs are arched, tails fuzzed, ears flattened and their teeth bared.

I wonder what prompted this Mexican stand-off which is starting to become most unpleasant. Rocky has probably taken exception to some slight sleight from Humbug.

Rocky punches the air taunting Humbug and egging him to fight.

I am the greatest,
I float like a flupperty and sting like an acker
You're just a woozel
Whose cheese slid off his cracker
You're gonna zilly yourself, you'll be so scared
Coz I am a tiger with my shiny teeth bared

'You talking to meow?' Humbug asks, in his deepest voice with his eyebrows raised.

Geez, even Bobcat de Niro would be shaking in his shoes.

'Hey guys, snap out of it will ya,' Maharani screeches. But the boys seem oblivious to her command.

Now the mezzing is really guttural and it looks like there's about to be catastrophic feeli-cuffs.

The boys start to crab sideways, neither giving ground. Their hackles are sticking up like they've stuck their tails in a power point. It looks like it's going to be on for old and young. Rocky starts some fancy footwork, like he's tripping the light fandango, and dodges from side to side trying to confuse his opponent.

We all crowd around them in a circle – which a boxing *ring* should be, by the way – then Raffles pushes his way into the ring.

'Okay, who wants to place a bet?' he says. 'Will it be Rocky the Boofhead or Humbug the Sweet?'

'But we haven't got anything to bet with,' Zsa Zsa observes. 'Oh, unless we bet tomorrow's breakfast or dinner perhaps.'

I like the sound of that, coz there's no doubting for a second that Rocky's gonna flatten Humbug; and two helpings of rations tomorrow would be neat.

'Just a moment now.' A brindle tortie with curly-tipped ears appears ringside. Choux-Fleur is her name, if I recall correctly. 'They need a referee, they can't have a hoogy without a referee,' she says.

Roger appears behind her and volunteers, stepping into the ring and gesturing to us all to take a step back. Raffles darts over to pen one, scales the wire and grabs the number card off the gate and hands it to Finny.

'Wait a minute,' Finny pipes up, 'they've got to be introduced properly.'

'Jeez, at this rate they'll have forgotten what they're fighting about,' Maharani says.

I nod at her in agreement. I'm suddenly aware of someone behind me. I turn and find myself face to face with the Colonel. He licks his paw and runs it through his whiskers then pushes past me into the ring.

'Allow me,' he says. He clears his throat and puffs out his chest. 'In the red collar, weighing in at six point five kilos, with several titles under his belt and the scars to prove it, all the way from pen nine is Rockeeee the Boofhead.'

Still looking mean as hell, Rocky nods, traces a 180 degree arc around the ring and manages to never take his eyes of Humbug.

'And in the blue collar, in his first heavyweight bout and ever-so-slightly the underquiffo, weighing in at five kilos, but don't be fooled by his name coz he's one mean feeli; from pen eight it's Huumbuuug the Sweet.'

Humbug raises one paw to acknowledge the crowd.

'Hang on,' Raffles calls out, 'place your bets, place your bets. Rocky's the odds-on favourite and Humbug's coming in at five to one. Hurry, hurry. No more bets after the bell's rung.'

Everyone mills around Raffles as he takes the bets. Finny stands on her hind legs, holding the number one in her front paws and tries to walk a circuit of the ring.

I see now what Maharani means about her balance: gorgeous face but about as much co-ordination as a three-legged feeli high on catnip. After a few flops and flounces she departs the ring.

Roger nods to Maharani and she shakes her head, whereon her bell signals the start of round one.

Rocky and Humbug eye each other a moment longer and then fly at each other. In an instant they're tangled in a Gordion knot and it's hard to differentiate one from the other. Tufts of fur float above them, and the mezzing is so loud I start to wonder whether Miss Steph can hear it from her house.

They sound like a hundred squeaky doors being opened at once as they roll around the floor like a huge, crazy furball. Occasionally, an identifiable limb sticks out, but from my vantage point it's impossible to tell who has the upper paw.

It's so loud that Lara and Zsa Zsa have their paws in their ears and strained expressions on their faces. Finny has her paw over her eyes. I'm guessing that, having led sheltered lives, they've never been ringside before. The whole episode reminds me of my fuddy.

'My fuddy was murdered to death in a hoogy,' I call out to anyone who can hear.

'When was that?' the Colonel asks.

'Oh, about three years ago.'

'Hang on, how old are you then?'

'Me? I'm two and a bit.'

'How big a bit?'

'Why? What's it matter?'

'Well, if you're only two and a little bit of a bit, then he couldn't have been your fuddy.'

I don't get what he means 'Why?'

'Coz, Juno, you said he was killed.'

'Oh, no, he survived it; got some good scars though.'

'But–'

We can barely hear the bell ringing and Maharani finds herself in the middle of the ring shaking her head wildly trying to make the combatants hear it. They're oblivious to her.

'I think,' says Big Dan stepping calmly into the ring, 'that there's got to be a peaceful way to sort out your differences.' He intrepidly puts his head into the scrum, grabs Rocky by the neck with one paw and Humbug with the other and pulls them apart.

'Hey, enough already you two. Didn't you hear the bell? Now, pray tell, just what was this disagreement all about anyway?'

'He said I smelt like I'd eaten my breakfast twice,' Rocky says.

'Is that it?' Big Dan shakes his head in bewilderment. 'And you honestly couldn't think up a good comeback for that?'

'She's coming, Miss Steph's coming!' Beethoven shouts. 'Back to your pens, quick.'

We all start skidding and sliding and running around like mad things trying to find our own pens. I fly into mine, turn and pull the gate until I hear the click of the latch. I hear the clicks of several other gates shutting and the odd *mehs* and *eewows* as some of my fellow inmates squabble over whose quarters are whose. Within a few seconds we're all in bed, smiling and quirrelling and congratulating ourselves for our perspicaticy.

'That fight reminds me of my Uncle Clawed,' I say for no particular reason.

In the midnight hours

'Who's a big boofhead then?' Miss Steph asks.

I can hear some very loud quirrelling and can only presume that Rocky's really turning on the pussano treatment.

'Hey, what's happened here boy? Your ear's bleeding, what *have* you been up to? You just wait there while I go get something for that.'

I hear Miss Steph walking back towards the door.

'Pttthh pthhhh… ' Rocky spits. 'Just as well she didn't see the mouthful of Humbug I just spat out.'

Everyone has a giggle. Then I hear the other Megsy and Choux-Fleur giggling between themselves.

'Yeah, I didn't think a feeli could get that fat either,' Choux-Fleur says, obviously in response to a comment from Megsy that I didn't hear.

'She's so fat she looks like a pumpkin with legs.'

Okay, so now my ears are pricked and so's my back. 'Yeah, well you call yourself a ginger? You're so faded, you've either spent too much time in the sun or you've been bitten by the insipid bug,' I spit back. 'And as for you, vegetable head, you must be really slow to have not been able to outrun those snails.' I hear no more giggling to that retort, so I figure they know where they stand with me now.

Miss Steph returns and I hear her performing first aid on Rocky.

'Now don't go licking that, boy,' she says.

I hear a kiss, followed by some more deafening quirrelling. Miss Steph starts doing the rounds and before long I can hear a crescendo of mehs and quirrelling as everyone gets their own bit of personal attention. The sounds of contentment are momentarily interrupted by Rocky.

'Pttthh pthhhh... Yuck, that tastes awful.'

I start to claw and pronkledonk my pillow in expectation. Just getting myself in the mood, you know.

'Ooh, you're such a gorgeous girl... your eyeliner is just so perfect,' Miss Steph says.

'Yes, yes I know,' Zsa Zsa agrees. 'I've been told I'm even more attractive than Ingrid Birman.'

I crack up. 'Yeah, and as funny as Phyllis Burmilla.'

'Oh, ha ha,' Zsa Zsa replies sarcatically.

'Yes you're just so beautiful,' Miss Steph continues, 'you look just like um–'

'Catty Zeta Jones? Nicole Kitten?' Zsa Zsa suggests.

'Blofeld's cat,' Miss Steph says. 'Yes, just like Blofeld's cat.'

That one's lost on me. Miss Steph is holding Zsa Zsa and stroking her, while looking through the wire window – at me. She shakes her head slowly. 'Some cats just get all the breaks, don't they Zsa Zsa?'

Zsa Zsa head butts her in agreement. 'Yes,' she quirrels, 'you just can't beat good breeding, can you Miss Steph. A true pedigree, that's me.'

'I'm sure she can't understand you, Zsa Zsa,' I point out.

'But you know,' Miss Steph whispers to Zsa Zsa, 'as far as I'm concerned, nothing beats a good old moggie. There's just no airs and graces with a moggie,' she whispers, and–

Wait a sec; was that a wink? Did she really wink at me?

Zsa Zsa immediately bristles and presses her paws into Miss Steph's chest trying to get as far from her face as possible.

'What's a moggie?' I ask her.

'A wuzzer. A stupid, ordinary wuzzer – like you,' Zsa Zsa spits.

'Oh, really?' I smile and poke my tongue out at her. She starts to look pre-schpitzo and I figure Miss Steph had better be careful. Hell hath no fury like a feeli scorned. Zsa Zsa jumps away from Miss Steph and I hear the thump as she lands back on her shelf.

'Oh, goodnight then, cranky pants,' Miss Steph says as she shuts Zsa Zsa's gate.

Ooh, ooh, she's coming. I start to pronkledonk my pillow again. I tip my head to the side slightly and then, as she approaches, I roll my head into a demi-ipwod.

Only special deuxjambs who I trust ever get my ipwod.

She looks quite funny upside down. She seems to get the hint though, as she gently scratches my upturned chin and neck. Now she's tickling my chest and armpit. I roll a bit more into a full-ipwod. And she starts to rub my tummy.

'Ooh ooh, ah ah… ooh,' I quirrel uncontrollably. My tongue flops out to catch a dribble drip.

'You sound like Megsy Ryan having an organism,' Maharani calls out.

'Next best thing,' I reply. 'And by the way–'

'Oh you're such a chubby bubby, a floppy moggie, a flabby slab, aren't you,' Miss Steph says as she rubs my tummy so vigorously I can't even speak.

I should be taking exception to her comments but then this just feels sooooo good. 'Flubby dubs, flabby flanks; oh you're just so squidgee, what a honey bunch.'

I start to wonder who's enjoying this more. I realise that I don't mind what names she calls me – so long as she calls me. She can say whatever she likes so long as I get this treatment every day. I quirrel as loud as I can and she rubs some more. I figure I've got this worked out now.

'Nighty night then, girl, you sleep tight now.'

'Yes, I will thank you. I couldn't be more relaxed if I tried. In fact I might just nod–'

I'm curled up in my favourite spot. Hayoo's rhythmic breathing is like a gentle shiatsu massage on my back. I regulate my breathing to match hers and I'm floating on a wave of euphoria. Life just doesn't get any better than this. But, hang on, why's she prodding me like that? She's still asleep and yet she's prodding me on the shoulder, softly at first and then harder and more urgently.

'What, what?' I wave my paw distractedly

'Juno, Juno wake up.'

'Huh?'

'Fuuuudgepuddle!' I hear the word the same moment I feel hot breath in my ear. My eyes snap open and I'm instantly brought back to reality and I'm eye to eye with the smallest face in the feeli world.

'What, Raffles? What's the big emergency? Is the place on fire or something?'

'No, don't be silly. But you *are* missing the party.'

'Party? Did I hear party?'

'Yep, we're having a midnight feast.'

Now I'm really awake. And I can smell tuna!

My feet barely touch the ramp before I hit the floor running. Everyone's there ahead of me in a big circle and they're all licking their lips and quirrelling contentedly. In the middle, a pile of kitzbitz is spilled out of a bag and there's a pile of flat, shiny green and silver things with tuna squidging out of them. *Yum!*

Red and Mars are performing a strange

67

manoeuvre. Red's stomping on one end of the shiny creature – probably to knock it out – and Mars is licking up the tuna as it spurts out its mouth.

I had no idea that was what they looked like before they were killed. Hayoo never had live ones, so I've only ever had them out of a can.

A few other dead ones are lying around. Big Dan is sitting there licking his paw and washing his face. He looks very satisfied. He puts his foot on one of the shiny things and flips it over to me.

'Here, I saved you one. We thought you were never going to wake up.'

'Huh? I just dropped off for a second or two.'

'More like two hours, girl; a good two hours.'

'You're kidding. Cor, it seemed like just a few seconds.' I start pawing the shiny creature. 'I see you've already killed it for me, thanks Big Dan.'

'Huh?' Big Dan pulls his head back a bit and frowns at me. 'What do you mean?' He takes a couple of steps towards me. 'Just step on this end and it'll squeeze out there.'

I follow his instructions and start lapping up the succulent treat. It suddenly dawns on me that this is probably not a regular occurrence.

'Where did this come from?'

'Well you can thank Raffles for this. Not only did he figure out how to open the door into the kitchen, he also worked out how to use the choppertine in the office to cut these open,' Big Dan explains.

With that, Raffles trots in the door with another one in his mouth. He comes towards me and drops it on the floor.

'Okay, who has only had one?'

'Me, me,' I say, jigging up and down.

'Well it's the last one, so make the most of it,' Raffles says.

'Yum, thanks kid.' I polish off the tuna in no time while keeping an eye on what everyone else is up to.

Lara seems to be teaching Choux-Fleur some nifty ballet manoeuvres; Humbug is licking a wound on his shoulder; Big Dan looks like he's trying hard not to fall asleep sitting up; Zsa Zsa is pacing up and down and gesturing at Maharani to copy her moves; the three Rs – Rabbit, Rog and Rocky – are deep in conversation and looking decidedly conspiratorial; Finny is looking ditzy, while singing *Oops I did it again;* and Monty, Red and Mars look like they're attempting some weird two-legged balancing act.

Well, they're an entertaining lot, I'll give them that. I feel a bit left out, I confess, so I wander back to my suite for a midnight zilly.

I realise now it was hours ago that I was contemplating what to make out of my kackapod paper. Between dizza and escaping our pens and boxing matches and midnight feasts, it's been quite a night.

I carefully pull the paper out of my kackapod with my teeth – managing to slide the pellets off into the kackapod without spilling any – and lay it on the floor to make sure I don't get it wet.

I step into the kackapod and circle around and shuffle the pellets to one end. I pause and look behind me to make sure it's a neat pile. Nope. A bit more adjustment. There. I squat to– Okay you don't need to know that. I stare at the corner of the pen, for no particular reason, it's just that that's the way I'm facing. My mind wanders off to Weeras, as it usually does when I'm concentrating on nothing much in particular.

I finally finish what turns out to be a substantial zilly and am much relieved. After doing a meticulous job of covering everything up so I can't smell it, I get to thinking about my new-found talent – origami. Who knew!

I'm thinking about a queekee, maybe a long-legged thing like the ones that prance around my front garden; like Hayoo does in her tall shoes, but more graceful than her.

I start with some accurately placed folds, a bit of batting and some elbow creasing and it starts to take shape.

'Whatcha making?' Maharani asks casually as she wanders into my pen.

'One of those long-legged queekees.'

'Hmm,' Maharani comments. She doesn't sound very convinced.

I look up at her and then do a double take. There's something strange about her face. 'What have you done to your eyes?'

'Oh yeah, do you like it? Zsa Zsa's just been showing me how to put eye liner on. Do you think I look sophisticated?'

'Um… sultry, very sultry.'

'Zsa Zsa says I look like Cleocatra, do you think so?'

'Cleocatra's a bit of a stretch. I'd have said, ah, Alice Cooper maybe.'

'Alice Cooper? Who's she? Is she very attractive?'

How can I not laugh? I mean, I thought I was thick sometimes. 'Yes, very,' I nod reassuringly. 'Anyway, as I was saying, I'm making one of those long-legged queekees.'

'So where are its legs?'

'Yeah, well that's the problem. I haven't got enough paper. So I guess it'll just be a long-legged queekee sitting down.'

'Why don't you just make a short-legged queekee?'

'Huh?' I'm just about to tell her to mind her own business when Raffles bowls up.

'Hey, that's neat,' he says, 'it looks like a flabinko sitting down.'

'Ha!' I laugh and pull a face at Maharani. 'See *he* knows what I'm doing.'

'Why don't you give the poor thing some legs?' Raffles asks.

'You shut up, Maharani,' I get in first before she even gets to open her mouth. 'Because I haven't got enough paper, that's why.'

'Oh I can fix that, stay right here, I'll be back in a sec.'

True to his word, he's back just about before he was gone,

and he's got several sheets of yellow paper in his mouth. He drops them on the floor and then paws one off the top.

'Here, have these. I'm gonna make another floomy out of this piece.'

'Thanks kid. Hey I could make all sorts of things out of this.'

I get to folding, but muck up the first leg, making it too short. A bit of on-the-spot redesigning and I turn the gammy leg into a beak. Big Dan appears at my gate. He's got a mouth full of empty tunas. He places them gently on the floor before speaking.

'I thought we'd better clean up the mess or Miss Steph will get suspicious. Maybe she'll just forget she had all these on the shelf in there. Who's going to help?'

'Yeah, yeah I'll help,' Raffles volunteers. Such an amiable young chap he is. Do anything for anyone, I get the impression. For some reason he reminds me of those slobbery, doofus bring-back quiffos. I wonder how someone so young could be so clued in. I don't know why, but he makes me think of my kisskies. I can only hope they turned out to be street smart like me and I hope they've discovered their talents. I didn't have enough time with them to teach them to have confidence in themselves.

'What's up?' Big Dan asks, startling me from my reveries. 'You looked really down in the dumps then.'

'Nah, I'm okay. I was just thinking about my kisskies. I had six you know. Beautiful they were.'

Big Dan tips his head as a sign of interest so I figure he wants to hear more. 'Yes, they were all different. Ori, he was really handsome – all black with just a tiny white spot on his chest, but he'd do *this* with his eyebrows and look very intelligent; enlightened, even. Arni, he was a really stocky little thing; a perfectly symmetrical teezee; he had the most beautiful markings. I'd look at him and wonder how I'd created something so perfect. Then there was Erna; Erna was gorgeous. She looked, well she looked just like me, but with not as much white. I'm sure she'll have grown up to be very attractive.

Unfortunately the same couldn't be said of Arelli. She was, ummm, plain; just plain and ordinary, a nondescript sort of black and brown. But she was clever and resourceful and she knew how to get her way; a bit of a bossy boots really. Inda was next. He was a bit smaller than the others and was fuzzy and grey, except for one foot which looked like he'd stepped in a saucer of yellum. And he was very, very mischievous but also a bit of a sooky pants and was always the first to come running to me with some drama or another. But he was lovely and he had the loudest quirrel I've ever heard.' I smile at Big Dan and he seems to acknowledge my pride. 'So there you have it.'

'But you've missed one, you said you had six.'

'Ooh,' I put my paw to my mouth, 'oops. The last one was Sizi, definitely the prettiest of them all. You know, I think she had a bit of all the others thrown in. Her coat was like a jigsaw puzzle, with black and white and ginger and grey and even some stripes; very hard to describe. She thought she was ugly; that when I made her I couldn't decide what I wanted, like an artist using up the leftover colours on her palette. But I used to tell her that she was the luckiest; that the other five were my experiments to determine the most attractive combination of colours. That always cheered her up.'

Big Dan nods in understanding. 'You sound like a very proud mother. I presume though that they all went to Weeras?' It was really more of a statement than a question.

'Yes, they all went separately. Goodness only knows where they are now.'

'So you only had one possel of kisskies?'

'Yes. Just the one. For some reason, after that, actually after that day at Slippery Sam's when I came home with a sore belly and a most unattractive square stubble here,' I point to my side, 'I just didn't have any bucho any more. And for some reason, the guys around the neighbourhood just didn't seem interested in me again. Why do you suppose that is Big Dan? Aren't I attractive any more?'

'Oh, on the contrary Juno, I think you're very attractive. It's just that the deuxjambs have taken away your bucho and your ability to have more kisskies, just as they've taken away my bucho to help make them.'

'Oh.' I pretend to understand. 'But what gives them the right to do that to us?'

'Well Juno, I've pondered that question myself for quite a long time. And I've come to the conclusion that it's because they don't want the world to have more of us than them. I think they'd feel, um, intimidated, you know?'

'Hey you could be right. It's sort of like us wishing there weren't so many quiffos around.'

'Yeah, sort of. But then the deuxjambs seem to like quiffos too, and it doesn't stop them limiting the number of mini-quiffs as well.'

'You mean quiffos get de-buchoed too?'

'Yes, they do.'

'Ha, ha. Well I never. So that means, let me get this straight, that means if quiffos weren't de-buchoed, there'd be squillions of them.'

'Yes, I guess so.'

'Maybe that's fair then. I guess if there were *that* many quiffos and mini-quiffs around, life would be pretty miserable for us, wouldn't it?'

'Now that you mention it, you're probably right about that. Anyway, at least you did get to have a possel; most feelis don't, you know. Except maybe the ecsotiques.'

'Hmm, that figures. Those darn pedigrees get all the breaks. Spoilt as they are.'

Big Dan gives me one of those you-shouldn't-have-said-that looks and I immediately realise my faux pas. 'Oh, sorry, I didn't mean you.' I wish I could take the words back.

'Hey girl, I'm a big boy. I wasn't about to take it personally you know.' He steps forward purposefully and dops my forehead and then steps back and smiles.

De-buchoed or not, I can't help quirrelling. Nor can I subdue the urge to dop him back. I feel so pussano I can barely sit up straight. I conjure this perfect image of Big Dan putting his kackapod right next to mine.

'Hey, that's a neat flabinko,' Big Dan says, interrupting my train of thought again. 'It's brilliant; so realistic.'

Oosh! I could hardly get any more blubbery. This guy just knows how to push my bucho buttons – even if I don't have them any more.

'Oh, thanks,' I say, coming over all embarrassed. I just can't look at him, coz it's not like I'm used to getting compliments.

'Just wait until Miss Steph sees that. She'll think you're a star. She'll want to display it somewhere. Hey you know, you could become famous. I mean not many feelis can do origami; at least none that I've heard of.'

'No. She won't even notice, I bet. She didn't notice my wimby yesterday. She just stepped on it and squashed it. Talk about deflating.'

'Maybe she didn't mean to. She mightn't have realised what it was. Hey, why don't we put it up on the shelf so she can't step on it. Maybe she'll notice it then.'

'I guess. It's worth a try.'

Pussyfootin' on the Ritz

I don't know what time it was that we finally went to bed, but at the moment I feel like I've got a rubber band stretched around my forehead. I groan just like Darling and Hayoo do when they have a late night and drink too much of that red stuff from those spindly glasses. Now I know just how they feel. I don't want to get out of bed either.

Funny, I haven't even been here 24 hours yet and, though they mightn't like to hear it, I haven't had time to miss Hayoo and Darling. It must be coz I now know what it means to go on a holiday. It sure beats climbing the wire with yawnism at AlCATraz.

But did I *really* tell Big Dan my whole life story last night? Uggh, I hope he didn't think it was too forward of me. Y'know, sometimes my tongue just runs off without me.

As I slowly open my eyes, I get that somefeeli's-watching-me frickle. I peek across and get the impression that Lara, Maharani and Beethoven are waiting for me to bestow some pearl of wisdom on them. They're all are lined up like nuckies in a shooting gallery.

But hang on – I focus my eyes better and acknowledge they're not actually looking at me. They're turning their heads from side to side like those open-mouthed sideshow clowns, or maybe spectators at Wimbledon.

Ah! It's then I see a furry blur buzz by, followed closely by two lots of deuxjambs' jambs. In a moment they're all going back the opposite way and almost falling over each other.

'This one's a live wire,' Maharani comments. 'They've been chasing him up and down for five minutes. He jumped out of his basket before they got the gate shut.' She giggles. 'It's nearly as funny as last night's boxing match.'

'Hey, calm down,' Zsa Zsa calls out to the escapee. 'You're giving me a headache. Just settle down; it's not that bad in here, none of us will bite you.'

The three whiz past my gate again. I feel like an extra in an episode of Keystone Kats. Miss Steph and the other deuxjamb don't seem to be gaining any ground on this speedster kisskie. I reckon he'd actually be able to catch Speedy Gonzalez. He's such a blur I can barely distinguish what colour he is, let alone what he actually looks like.

'Attennnn hut!' The Colonel calls out, marshalling his most officious tone. It works. The wayward kisskie comes skidding to a halt in front of his pen, while Miss Steph and the other deuxjamb bump into each other.

'Behave yourself, young man! This behaviour will not be tolerated under my watch. Now get to your pen and show Miss Steph just what a good kisskie you can be.'

'Y...y...yes sir, absolutely sir, s...sorry sir.'

'And don't stutter, you sound s...s...stupid. Now get down and give me twenty.'

'Yes sir, r...r...right sir.'

The Colonel starts counting: one, two, three. I can't quite see up the aisle but I gather the new arrival is obeying the Colonel's order. I wonder just what it is he's giving twenty of. I don't have to wonder long as Rocky calls out, 'I think he meant puss-ups kid, not starpaws'.

'What on earth was all that about, Coalpit?' the strange deuxjamb asks. 'You silly, naughty boy, now get in there and behave yourself. Obnoxious cat. I can't imagine why I picked him.' She's obviously talking to Miss Steph.

I hear the gate click and she and Miss Steph are off, without a goodbye, a fare-thee-well, an adieu or even a second glance. Not a nice deuxjamb, that one. Trust me, I can tell.

'Gee, wouldn't want to interrupt your holiday plans,' I say.

'Mmm. Not the friendliest deuxjamb I've come across,' Maharani says. 'She reminded me of my neighbour Herman's deuxjambs. He's shut out all the time and they just ignore him. I don't know why they got him in the first place. His coat looks like a dreadlock holiday and, nice as he is, I just *know* he's got virtles – he's always scratching. Maybe his deuxjambs are worse than this one. I mean, they'd never think to put him in a place like this when they go away. My deuxjambs are always going in to feed him when his go off. He tells me I don't know how lucky I am to have such obliging deuxjambs.'

'Yeah, I s'pose when you come to think of it, this one's deuxjambs wouldn't have put him in here if they didn't love him.'

'Maybe you're right,' Maharani says.

'Wheee-oww!' A plaintive cry pierces the morning murmurs. 'I'm not supposed to be here. They've made a mistake. I'm not supposed to be here, I'm innocent! I never did anything.'

Maharani and I shake our heads at each other.

'Oh dear,' I say, 'he's going to be a hard case'.

'Mmm,' Maharani agrees, 'just as well he wasn't taken to AlCATraz. Innocent or not, he'd really have something to worry about there.'

'Hey, don't worry little one, we'll make you feel at home,' Raffles calls out.

'Yes, you won't mind it once you've been here a while,' Finny adds.

'Nobody's going to hurt you here,' Big Dan says soothingly.

Our attempts to soothe the young one seem merely to exacerbate his feeling of desertion and despair. He starts to sob and for some reason the sound makes my maternal instincts kick in. I want to rush to his pen and console him but I'm stuck in here of course.

'There, there honey, c'mon it's not so bad,' I call out pathetically.

The sobbing gets louder and louder and nothing any of us says seems to console him.

'Oh, I can't stand that,' Raffles calls out. 'We've gotta figure out how to cheer him up, the poor thing. Maybe we could tell him some funny stories or put on a concert or something.'

'Or a cataret show,' Finny suggests. 'We can all come up with an act. That should cheer him up.'

'Great idea,' Maharani nods, 'Finny, you can sing a song obviously, Lara can do a dance, Rocky and I can do our balcony scene.'

'I'll be MC,' the Colonel says, 'and I have a great repertoire of jokes.'

'I have a number I can do. It's called *I'm a Lumbercat and I'm Okay*,' Big Dan offers. 'And I bet Beethoven could do a mime act if we suggested it to him.'

'Yeah,' I chime in, 'we could introduce him as Ludwig Marceau. Oh, and I know a great cataret song we could do if anyone wants to join me. It would be a fine opening number. We'd need to rehearse it a bit. We should spend the afternoon planning and be ready to start at eight o'clock. Everybody up for it?'

I'm almost deafened by the resounding cheers and Juniper's siren which starts up before any of us has the chance to put our paws to our ears.

'Hey, Beethoven, do you want to join in?'

No answer.

'He can't hear you, stoopid,' Humbug says.

79

'I could tap it out on the wall in Morse code,' the Colonel suggests, 'maybe he'd feel it'.

'You know Morse code?' Raffles asks.

'Well, I know some of the letters.'

'Yeah, which ones?'

'S, O and – um – S.'

'Very useful,' Raffles smirks. 'You could tell him to soss off then, or s…s…something like that.'

'Does anyone know sign language?' I offer. I'm met with silence. 'Guess not.'

'This could be nearly as much fun as a DDD, except there won't be any deuxjambs of course,' Zsa Zsa says.

I wait a moment before I ask the obvious question coz I don't want to appear too dumb. 'What's a DDD, Zsa Zsa?'

'Oh, don't you know? Silly question – of course you wouldn't. A DDD is a Deuxjambs Display Day. But only pedigree feelis ever get invited. It's a real privilege to go to one of course. It's really neat coz you get your own private feelichaise, which is a special viewing box, like front row dress circle, all lined with satin or velvet. Then the deuxjambs parade past and try all sorts of things to get you to pick them.'

'Pick them for what?'

'To win, d'oh.'

'To win what? I don't get it,' I confess.

'Well, there's all sorts of categories like um, the nicest smile, the friendliest, the nastiest, the fattest, the smelliest, the most obnoxious, you know, that sort of thing.'

'Oh, so is that all there is to it?'

'No, it's a bit more complicated than that. The lead up to it is quite important too. You get your own deuxjambs to make a really big fuss over you beforehand – y'know like a princess going to a ball. You get bathed, blowdried, combed and coiffed; you get a manicure and they put smelly stuff on you and basically they get you looking really spiffy. Of course the secret is not to make it too easy for them. I mean, you have to make them feel you're doing all this under sufferance, like any self-respecting princess would do with her servants. But anyway, you really have to dress up for these things – it's like going to the opera.'

'Sounds awful to me, just like hell. Don't tell me they sing.'

'Nah, nothing like that. They just walk past and stick their faces up close to you and make a lot of "ooh aah" noises and make faces at you to try to make you like them.'

'So, what if you don't? Or if you get sick of it?'

'Oh, that's easy. You can demonstrate feelichatra, coz you can always get in behind the curtain at the back of your box. Or you can just yarl at them until they go away; or maybe chuck a schpitzo coz that's sure to make them move.'

'Oh, okay but what if you like them?'

'Simple, just turn on the pussano.'

'But how do you decide who wins?'

'It's a consensus thing. Obviously if one stands up or comes past and gets a lots of yarls and pfutts, well that's not gonna be the winner of the friendliest or the nicest smile is it?

'So you go by the yarlometer for those sorts of categories and then the pussanometer decides the nice qualities. But, oh, I almost forgot, we also get a turn to make individual selections – that's sort of like a mutual adoration section of the show.

'One of the deuxjambs, usually just somebody in a white coat, takes you out of your feelichaise and holds you up in the air so you can get a better view of all the deuxjamb contestants. White coat then sort of twists and contorts you a bit to make sure you don't miss the deuxjambs lurking in the corners behind the other feelichaises; which is very accommodating really. Then white coat puts you on a table and natters on about this and that – they go on about coats and skin, and eyes and ears to give us an idea of what attributes we should vote for.

'That bit's pretty boring once you've done it a few times but it does give you a better perspective about who to vote for. Because obviously if the contestants sneer a bit or shake their heads, you're not gonna vote for them. But if they nod and smile and maybe clap, you know they're trying really hard to get your vote.'

'But what's the point of it? I mean I'm not really all that interested in other deuxjambs; I like mine well enough but–'

'Well you know how far deuxjambs will go to please us,' Zsa Zsa interrupts. 'I assume this is a way for them to get recognition for it. Sort of like the Acatemy Awards, but with different judging criteria. So this is not about how good *they* think they are, it's about how good *we* think they are.'

'Oh, I get it. So is there like a grand prize? Y'know, like the best actor?'

'Yes, the one they aspire to most is the title of 'Deuxjamb of the Show – servitude award'.'

'Servitude?'

'Yep. Servitude. Obviously the whole point is finding the deuxjamb with the best attributes. Um, maybe a better way to explain it is the one we'd most like to have take care of us. And trust me, they try really hard to get your vote. You'd be surprised how many have told me they'd like to take me home so they could look after me. They've pledged their complete devotion to me. I mean, I could have started a bidding war at one show – I had four deuxjambs trying to outdo each other for my affections. They were just about falling over each other to fuss over me. It was a bit irky actually – it made me feel like *I* was the one on show.' Zsa Zsa riffles her fur in disgust.

'But you know, at the end of the day if you're happy enough with the deuxjambs you've got, why would you change? You'd only have to teach the new ones how to behave. Who could be bothered, I ask you?' Zsa Zsa turns, plonks onto her rump to lift her hind leg, and licks her ooti.

I take much of what she says with a grain of kitzbitz but it makes me wonder. 'So how come I've never been invited to a vote?'

'Oh, as if!' she cackles maniacally as she lifts her face out of her ooti. 'You've got to be *very* special to be invited to a DDD. I mean, it's a bit like one of those shows where everyone performs for the lady deuxjamb with the jewels on her head and then they shake her hand afterwards. Oh, and everyone has to catsy.'

'What for?'

'I'm not really sure, I think they're trying to look up her dress.'

'Oh.'

We all spend the afternoon rehearsing and it takes that long just for Lionel and Humbug to learn the words for my opening number. It's no mean feat, since Lionel has a very short memory, Humbug's still a bit battle-scarred, and neither of them can hold a tune. The others seem okay, although Finny keeps trying to get us all back on pitch.

It's the choreography that's a problem though coz, despite Lara's best efforts, none of us can understand a darn thing she's saying and, I hesitate to mention, none of us has ballerina bones in us – we look more like accidental break-dancers.

But by the time Miss Steph has served up our dinner, given us all a cuddle, changed over our kackapods and gone off to Weeras, we're ready for Raffles to let us loose onto the stage.

As we all line up in front of the newbie's condo, a collective frickle makes everyone's fur stand on end, like we've all stuck our tongues into a toaster. Stagefright, I guess.

I can barely see the homesick kisskie. Cowering behind his kackapod, he just looks like a blob of blackish, or maybe grey, fuzz. Hopefully our little show will cheer him up a bit. I quickly scan all the performers and they all nod their readiness, so I give our self-appointed MC, the Colonel, the nod. He starts by welcoming everyone – like we weren't all already here anyway – and starts with a joke.

'What do you get if you cross a sailboat with a patisserie?'

'Don't know, tell us Colonel,' Raffles says.

'A catameringue, hahahaha.'

'Ugggh,' we all cringe.

'All right then. What do you call a feeli that's swallowed a nucky?'

Everyone shakes their heads.

'A duck-filled fattypuss.'

'Ha ha ha,' we all crack up laughing. Now that *is* funny.

The Colonel continues. 'And now, introducing for the very first time on stage at the Lap of Luxury, the talk of Feelidom, straight from their condos, the ten and only Ziegfield Feelis with *Pussyfootin on the Ritz*!'

I do the count-in and everyone starts the little steps Lara taught us; but we're all so busy trying to remember the steps, we forget most of the words:

> *If you're blue da da da da da da,*
> *Why don't you go where feelis kiss,*
> *Pussyfootin' on the Ritz.*

I realise all too soon that we're all out of step, but I hope the little kisskie won't notice; I mean, we really didn't get much time to rehearse. The singing's also not how I'd heard it in my head, but hey, at least we're trying.

I see the little kisskie raise his head slightly and then quickly duck it again in fear. I try to rally everyone to sing in tune, but it doesn't really help, so at the end of the chorus I give the throat-cut signal, which everyone sees except Humbug, who embarrasses himself dreadfully by singing the next line woefully out of tune.

Once the floor is clear, Monty introduces Beethoven, leading him to centre stage and giving him the intro. We all watch expectantly as he begins his mime act. I'm blowed if I can figure out what he's doing, but then I can't see his face.

We all give him a hearty applause when he's finished but Monty has to turn him around so he can see us clapping. He nods his appreciation and takes a small bow.

Little kisskie, however, still doesn't move from the back of his pen. Lara performs a lovely ballet solo, Raffles tries some conjuring and Big Dan performs his number, making me go all gooey again with his mellifluous and husky voice. I give him a wink and blow him a kiss as he departs the stage area.

But none of their efforts has moved dear kisskie. We all look at each other and shrug in defeat. Looks like it's going to be up to Finny to charm him out of his despair.

After her introduction, she clears her throat and begins,

You are so beautiful, to me...

My hair starts to stand on end a bit. I think even Joe Cocker-Spaniel would be moved. Her voice is so pure and clear. I can feel my jaw dropping and I'm simply unable to pull it up again. I've never heard anything so beautiful and I'm so transfixed I barely notice the fuzzy grey kisskie edging to the front of his pen. He's also spellbound and it's obvious Finny's voice has melted his heart too. I feel all warm and fuzzy as I watch her brilliant performance.

But just as she's on her last refrain, something tugs my attention back to her private audience. I squint a little to refocus on him and my heart skips a beat.

It can't be… surely not. He moves a little and, as he does, I see his yellum-coloured foot. I can't believe it. It is!

'Inda, Inda,' I call out as I cross the floor in a single move, unceremoniously upstaging Finny.

The kisskie turns his head to me and immediately his face brightens.

'Umbi, Umbi,' he squeals as he recognises me.

A tail of two kisskies

I'm so overwhelmed at seeing one of my kisskies again I almost forget my manners. Everyone's crowding around us, having obviously cottoned on to the elation emanating from this umbi and dos reunion. So when Inda and I have finished smothering each other with all the fuzpah sentiments we can muster, I start the introductions.

'Everyone, this is my number five kisskie – in order of birth, not in favouritism, that is. This is my Inda.' Everybody comes forward in turn to meet Inda.

'Oh, he's quite a handsome young thing, isn't he,' Zsa Zsa comments. I smile proudly and nod.

'For a wuzzer,' she adds, so I poke my tongue out at her.

'Very pleased to meet you, dossy,' Monty says politely. He turns to me. 'Excuse me for being so presumptuous as to try to discipline your dos earlier.'

'Oh that's all right, a firm paw never goes astray.'

'Hey Juno, how come he doesn't look anything like you?' Raffles asks. 'I mean I look just like my umbi and all my erries and dorries.'

'Well you see, Raffles, my own erries and dorries were all different. Maybe that's just how it is with wuzzers, and Inda's erries and dorries are also all different.'

'So what does Inda's fuddy look like?'

'Um, well he was black, I think, or maybe grey, or teezee even. Actually I'm not all together sure. It was dark, you see and, there was probably more than one anyway.'

'Oh,' Raffles shrugs as though he understands.

'Typical of a wuzzer,' Zsa Zsa butts in. 'Pedigrees *always* know who their father is. That's the one good thing about deuxjambs, they go to a lot of trouble to introduce us queens to only the crème de la crème of males of our breed. No way would we ever associate with just any neighbourhood tom. I mean, goodness me, just imagine if my perfect genes got interfered with! The shame would be unbearable,' she says haughtily.

Inda ignores her interruption. 'You mean you don't you know who my fuddy is?' he asks.

I feel my face flush a bit. How do I tell my dos that I don't know who his fuddy is? I have to think quick. 'Your fuddy is a very handsome feeli who lives around my neighbourhood.' Hopefully that will suffice. After all, very few feelis get to meet their own fuddy.

'I'd love to meet him and so would Arelli. We often wonder about him.'

'Arelli? You mean you know where Arelli is?'

'Oh yeah, I see her all the time. She lives just down the road from me. She's got really lovely deuxjambs. They even let her sleep on their bed, they warm her yellum for her, and she's got this big waterhole in the ground with little orange wimbies for her to catch.

'I've tried to catch them but they're too quick for me, but she let me try one of hers once; it was really sweet and crunchy.

'I always know when she's coming to visit because she's got a little jingly thing on her chokeystrap which makes it difficult for her to sneak up on anything. The queekees always hear her coming and fly away before she gets anywhere near them.'

I'm smiling. Beaming, in fact. I'm so happy to hear that another of my kisskies is doing fine.

'So what about you, what are your deuxjambs like, Inda? I didn't get a very good feeling about the one who brought you in.'

'Oh, they were fine at first. They cuddled me lots and played games with strings and balls and let me sleep on the bed. Honey was really fat and she'd let me go to sleep on her belly, but then she went away for a few days and came back thin, with a squawking mini-deuxjamb.

'Since then they don't seem to care about me. They shut me out most of the time. Except if it's raining they let me in the room with the big white boxes that swallow their empty clothes and grumble a lot.

'So I just entertain myself most of the time. I'd love to go and live with Arelli, but she already has to share her house with another feeli and a big blonde quiffo who's always slobbering over her. She really loves them though and she's very happy,' Inda says.

'What do they call her?'

Inda snorts. 'Pixie. Can you believe it? She much prefers Arelli. But then Pixie's not as bad as Coalpit – that's what I'm called at home. Why do deuxjambs give us such silly names and expect us to come to them when they call? I don't get it, Umbi.'

'Problem is darling, we can understand them, but they can't understand us. It's a constant struggle for us to try to educate them as mostly they're pretty slow on the uptake; they just don't *get* us.

'Admittedly, some of them try hard and every now and then there'll be a moment, like they've had some sort of epiphany, when you really think they understand. But then they go and do something really stupid like changing the furniture around or turning on the plug-in sucker dragon or waking you up in the middle of a really good mindmove to Weeras. And you realise that they just haven't learned *anything*.

'But then they try to make up for our pfutts or our schpitzos by giving us extra kitzbitz or yellum, so eventually we forgive them.'

'Well that explains a lot. Here I've been thinking they're all just stooooopid.'

'Some are most definitely stoopid, Inda. But others can be trained to know what we want; it just takes time and patience. You're still young; you have to persevere, Inda-mine.'

'Oh,' Inda nods with a know-it-all-now air.

'I'm just so pleased to know where two of my kisskies are.' I quirrel loudly and Inda smiles back. 'I'd love to know where the others are.'

'Huh, that's easy Umbi, you just put their names into *Feelibook* on the Intercat, and you'll probably find them.'

Inda might as well be talking in Egyptian Mau to me for all the sense he's making, and he looks at my nonplussed face with amusement.

'Ohrr Umbi, haven't you ever checked out *Feelibook*? You can find out anything on *Feelibook*, and if not *Feelibook* then *Doodle* or *Yapuss.*'

I shake my head at him. 'I'm sorry Inda, I'm just not up with all this latest technology.'

'Geez Umbi, it's not like you're *that* old. Don't your deuxjambs have a puterbox? I mean I get on ours every night after everyone else has gone to sleep. It's amazing the stuff you can find out.'

'Like what? What could I possibly want to know that I could learn off a puterbox?'

'Where would I start? It'd be much easier if I could *show* you, but of course there doesn't just happen to be a puterbox lying around here does there?'

'No, but there's one in the office,' Raffles pipes in. 'I'll go turn it on,' he offers cheekily, relishing the prospect of demonstrating his ingenuity once again. He trots out the door with his tail jiggling in the air.

A few of us look at each other and shrug.

'Might as well, c'mon,' Inda says.

We all take up positions in the office, ensuring we're not blocking the view of anyone behind us. I score the comfy chair, sharing it with Inda, who's busy tapping away on the little square things with letters on them. The screen flickers and flashes; there's so much to take in I don't know where to look first. Inda plays with a funny round thing with a tail beside the computer, tapping it and pushing it around. He's not even watching what he's doing with it. It just looks like a plastic woozel to me.

'What's that?' I giggle. 'It looks like a woozel.'

I think I'm being really clever until I'm met with a loud chorus of: 'It *is* a woozel stupid.'

'Oh.' I decide to keep my mouth shut, but I'm finding it hard to resist trying to catch the little arrow flying around the screen.

'So Umbi, what do you want to know?' Inda asks.

'That's like the 64,000 tuna question. Well, I'd like to know where Ori, Arni, Erna and Sizi are. I'd like to know how to find Hamish the Handsome. I'd like to know why Garfield is *so* popular and whose poor tail is always being trodden on when Mariah Catty sings. I'd like to know why Hayoo and Darling don't give me yellum *every* night. I'd like to know why queekees have so many bones. Um, I'd like to know why those deuxjambs in dresses try to make sounds like us with those little bags with pipes–'

'Hey, just one thing at a time, Umbi,' Inda says.

'Okay, okay, so how do we find my other kisskies? Do we just put in their name and it tells us where they are?'

'It's not quite that simple; it's going to depend whether they're into Feelibook or whether they have their own weblike or not. And if their deuxjambs don't have a puterbox then it's going to be a bit tricky. But we'll give it a try. So we'll start with Ori. We need to know when and where he was born – that'll narrow it down from anyone else called Ori.'

'Oh, well, that's easy. He was born in the morning at home,' I advise smugly.

Everyone cracks up laughing.

'What?'

'I think you need to be just a bit more specific than that,' Big Dan says smoothly from right behind me. 'And, by the way, who's Hamish the Handsome?'

'Oh, he's just someone I used to know. Why? You're not jealous are you?'

'Don't be silly. Jealousy is a characteristic that a pure-bred Maine Coon like me simply does not countenance. It would be beneath my dignity to be so, er, undignified. Now, getting back to the issue at hand.'

'Now c'mon Umbi, do you remember the date and you must know where you live; where we were born.'

'Yes, yes I do remember the date. It was just after the house was filled with all those deuxjambs sitting around the table with silly hats on, handing each other shiny things from under the tree they'd brought into the napping room. Never can figure out why they bring a tree inside, but they do seem to do it every so often.

'Anyway, it was between about then and that awful night when it sounded like the sky was exploding and Hayoo and Darling let all their deuxjambs friends into our house, and they were all stumbling around trying to spill sticky stuff on me out of their glasses, and holding me while they pretended to dance. It was embarrassing and not fun at all.'

'Oh, so between Christmas and New Years then – last week of December,' Zsa Zsa says authoritatively.

'Huh?' I can't figure out how she worked that out so quick – she wasn't even there.

'Can you recall what day of the week it was?' she asks.

'Yes actually, it must have been a Friday, coz I got tuna for dinner, I always get tuna on Fridays. Just like here – funny that.'

'It's a cattolic thing,' the Colonel comments.

Zsa Zsa and Raffles both pull funny faces like they're working out something in their head.

'So it must have been December the 27th,' they blurt out in unison.

Inda taps on the black keys and plays with the woozel again. 'So what's the address where I was born umbi?'

'Hmm. Yes…' I pause and then nod at everyone in the circle around me. 'It's um, well it's a sort of creamy, yellum-coloured house.'

'Geez Umbi, even *I* know that and I only saw the outside once, through the holes in the box the day I got taken away. But what's the *address*?'

'Oh, I don't know. I guess I just don't pay much attention to that sort of thing,' I confess. If I could have my life over, I realise there'd be lots of things I would make a point of finding out so I wouldn't look so dumb in front of one of my own kisskies.

'Well, we're not going to get very far if we don't know the address,' Inda says dejectedly.

'Ah, too easy,' Raffles says as he pushes his way past Maharani and Zsa Zsa across the desk. Zsa Zsa overbalances and falls to the floor, catching a claw in the carpet.

'Oh darn, I've broken another fingernail.'

'The address will be in Miss Steph's file,' Raffles says, pawing open the lid of the box on the corner of the desk.

The rest of us tut and nod our heads in that gesture that recognises our collective stupidity.

'Hey, Fudgepuddle, what's your surname?' Raffles asks.

Inda's head swings around so quick his eyes wobble in their sockets, as he gives me squizzical. 'What did he call you, Umbi? Fudge – ha-ha – puddle. Ha ha.'

Now I just want to curl up and die.

'It's a term of endearment, love. Miss Steph thinks I'm pretty special and she only gives her own names to *special* feelis,' I explain, hoping to sound convincing.

'It's still pretty funny, but.'

I give him a wink and a nod. 'Now, my surname is...' I roll my eyes up towards the ceiling as though that's going to help me think. 'Um, I know it, I do, I think it starts with W.'

'Oh goodness, don't tell me you don't know that either,' Zsa Zsa says with a shaking of her head.

'Doesn't matter,' Raffles pipes up. 'Miss Steph's got pictures of all of us in this file, it's like an antiquated *Feelibook*. Oh look, here's Zsa Zsa– Oh, ha ha, she mustn't have had any make-up on when this was taken. Not very flattering...'

Before Raffles can continue, Zsa Zsa has leap-hibbied over Maharani and snatched the picture in her teeth. She sets to chewing it, working her jaws vigorously until there's nothing left of the card. 'I was only young then and I was having a bad fruff day,' she says as she tries to spit out a bit of paper stuck to her tongue.

'Oh and look, here's me,' Raffles announces as he holds his photo card up for everyone to see. 'Did you ever see such a good-looking guy? She's already done my card. That was quick.'

'Not too bad for a bug-eyed marsupial,' Humbug replies.

'Well at least I know what colour I am,' Raffles spits back, 'I'm sure you couldn't say for sure whether you're a white feeli with black blotches or a black feeli with white blotches. Probably you had a white mother and a black father–'

'And what's wrong with that?'

'Nuffin, I guess. It's surprisingly actually that you didn't come out grey when you think about it,' Raffles jokes.

'Oh funny ha ha,' Humbug snorts.

Raffles continues to rummage through the file box, working his way from the back to the front. 'Ah, ha, here we are. Megsy Campbell. Yeah, I can see how you could have thought it started with W.'

'Campbell, that's it, I knew I'd know it when you said it. Okay Inda, so try Ori Campbell,' I say tapping my dos on the shoulder.

'And your address is: 23 Fletcher Street, Parrot Point,' Raffles announces.

Inda clicks away on the woozel and as I stare at the screen I'm completely gobsmacked as an image of my Ori, admittedly a little older and wiser looking – but unmistakably my Ori – appears in a little box.

'What does it say, what does it say?' I'm so excited there's a risk of me zillying on the spot. 'Where is he?'

'Wow, he still lives in Parrot Point, so maybe he's not too far away. But his name's now Brian Buttrock. Look there's a clipping here from the *Parrot Point Press* with a picture of him. Look, it says: BRIAN THE CUTEST CAT.'

Everybody falls about laughing and I nearly fall of the chair.

Inda reads the caption aloud. 'Pictured with his blue ribbon, nine-month-old Brian, owned by Grace and Graham Buttrock of Graham Street and shown by their son Graham, was named cutest cat at the Parrot Point Primary Pet Parade. Well we shouldn't have too much trouble finding him when we get out of here.'

'Oh look,' Inda says, clicking onto Ori's bio, 'it says here that his interests are chasing flupperties, flower arranging and – hehehe – macramé. Mmm, um, think I need to have a word with my big dorry, you know, before everyone starts talking.'

I shake my head in surprise. And to think I

95

thought I'd taught them all so well. I'm so pleased he seems happy and of course I love him just the same, but I decide to change the subject. 'So what about Erna, Arni and Sizi?'

Inda types in Erna Campbell, with the birthdate and address. We all wait for a few moments before a face *everybody* recognises unrolls onto the screen.

'Corrrr,' everyone breathes in unison. My jaw just drops and my tongue curls like a roller coaster. We're all looking at none other than the new talk of Catzeltown, the latest kisskie star of Hollypudd, Dacata Fanny.

'This, this can't be! But it is – it's my Erna. How could I have not realised? Oh I always knew she was going to be famous.' I grin so wide my jaws start to ache. 'So much talent, I didn't know we had it in the family.

'Hmpph,' I pull a smug face at Zsa Zsa, 'makes your acting efforts look a bit pale doesn't it? She's my jes… Dacata Fanny. AKA Erna Campbell. I can't believe it. And to think I might never have known, if it weren't for *Feelibook*. What a wonderful, wonderful thing.'

'Hey look everyone, she's got her own weblike, www.dacatafanny.cat.' Inda clicks the woozel and suddenly the screen changes. There's tons of pictures of Erna-now-Dacata. In one, she's pictured with Tomcat Cruise, her fur all tatty and her mouth wide open like she's screaming; and in another with Denzel Washingup, in which her fur's all tatty and her mouth is wide open like she's screaming. Then there's a photo of her with fellow kisskie star, Haley-Paw Catmint. The words that go with that one has Dacata denying that there's any budding relationship between the two and she quotes, 'We did nothing more than sniff each other's ootis. There was nothing romantic about it.'

Another little box on the screen lists her filmy-ography to date. So far there's been seven (but then she's still very young I tell myself) and I can't believe I've never seen any of them. Okay, so I don't get out all that much.

First was *I am Sam the Cat*, then *Tomcats*, then *Cat in the Hat* and the most recent, *Nine Lives*. But now she's up for two Acatemy Awards as best co-star in *Catfight of the Worlds* with Cruise, and in *Cat on Fire* with Washingup. Wow, I'm blown away.

'Hey, looks like you've got a famous jes,' Big Dan says nudging me. 'I expect you'll be wanting to go to Hollypudd to see her and bask in her fame.'

I'm too moosh-thwacked to think about that, but, 'Hmmm,' I ponder aloud, 'how on earth would I get there?'

'I know, I know,' blurts Raffles. 'I've got a mate who works for FeeliFreight and he's always talking about this other guy called umm, Jack the Cheek or is it John the Lip?' Raffles looks squizzical at the ceiling.

'Jock the Nose,' the Colonel pipes in. 'I think you mean Jock the Nose, that crazy Scottish gofer.'

'Jock the Nose, what a silly name,' I giggle.

'They call him that because he knows everything,' Raffles says. 'Oh, and so they don't draw attention to his ears.'

'Och aye,' the Colonel says in a poor attempt at a Scottish accent, 'he's very self conscious about his ears. I don't know why. Every other Scottish Fold I've seen has daft ears as well, but he hates anyone mentioning them.

'But he always wants to know the ins and oots of your ooti that one. He's got his paw on the pulse of every feeli databank there is. Always got his nose in everything and there's not much he doesn't know. If you need a fake ID he knows where to go; if you want to find a missing feeli he can help; if you want to travel to New York Kitty he'll tell you the cheapest way to get there, and if you've got pedigree blood *anywhere* in your background, he'll know.'

'He sounds like a very handy fellow to know,' I remark, stating the obvious. I start thinking about the logistics of travelling over the seas to Hollypudd. I mean I can't just take off without a second thought for Hayoo and Darling. I have to accept that it's not really a practical idea, but that's not going to stop me thinking about it.

'I spose it figures that I'd have another famous actor in the family. If I could go to Hollypudd to see her, I might also be able to look up my fourth cousin, Clawed Eastwood. I've never met him, but I hear he's a big bloke, big as a lion. That's why he got the lead role in *Thunderfoot and Lightbulb*. He's been in lots of movies like *Where Queekees Dare, A Pawful of Dollars, The Good, the Bad and the Cuddly,* and, of course, *Escape from AlCATraz.* Oh, and I nearly forgot, *Absolute Powerpoint* in which he plays a catburglar.'

'You mean, you're related to Clawed Eastwood?' everyone asks at once. Their jaws all level with their elbows.

'Yeah. Well, he's a pretty distant relation. As I said, I've never met him and he wouldn't know me from a bowl of kitzbitz.'

'But even so,' Zsa Zsa says, 'I have to confess that almost puts me to shame. I mean Clawed Eastwood is my absolute most favourite actor. I always loved that classic line: *Go ahead! Make me play!*'

'I like his movie, *Grand Torana*,' the Colonel adds.

'Hey Fudgie,' says Big Dan, you wouldn't even have to leave the country to visit your jes. Look. All her filmys were made at Hollypudd on the Gold Coast.'

'Well there you go,' says the Colonel, 'Jock the Nose would have no trouble at all getting you there.'

Inda suddenly starts doing starpaws, and, in an excited voice, says, 'Hey Umbi, look at this. It's a picture of Sizi. She looks strange, like she's in a trance and she's got all sorts of weird jewellery on.'

I peer at the small picture on the screen; it looks like a catad. Before I even think to ask, Inda has clicked the woozel to enlarge the picture. Over Sizi's head are the words: *Finding Feelichatra.*

Inda starts to read the catad out loud: 'Find your feeli-zen, your inner hyla-chi, revisit your kisskiedom, uncover your past incatations, and learn how to make the most of your 99 lives.'

'Oh good grief, what a pile of kerfooey,' sniffs Maharani.

'It's obviously pitched at those who believe in this sort of woo woo nonsense.' I say.

'Hey, Sizi is not just the face of the catad. It says here she's just graduated as a medium,' Inda says.

'A medium what?' I ask.

'Oh Umbi,' Inda groans.

G.I. Juno

So Sizi is a clairvoyant, psychit feeli, who specialises in teaching the arts of feelichatra, hyla and, according to her bio, stimpledits.

Geez, even I haven't mastered feelichatra; it takes a long time to perfect that. I mean there's been plenty of times I think I've succeeded only to have Hayoo find me anyway. And very few feelis ever get the hang of hyla; most of us *never* learn to predict what a deuxjamb is about to do.

So I'm guessing Sizi must have a natural gift for vanishing into thin air. I get to wondering how it is that one of my own kisskies has learnt so much, so quickly. I can't determine whether to be proud of her or suspicious.

Obviously Inda is thinking the same thing.

'Corr, I can't believe an errie of mine is into all this woo woo stuff. Anyway, how could she know all this?' he says.

'I can't imagine, Inda, but I *can* say she certainly didn't learn it from me. As you know, I never got the chance to teach any of you any of this. I mean if I could predict what Darling and Hayoo were going to do next—'

'The secret of hyla, Fudgie,' Humbug

addresses me authoritatively, 'is the fact that all deuxjambs are predictable; we just have to know how to be a step ahead of them.

'Bear in mind of course that some are clever at disguising what they're going to do, while others telegraph everything. For example, I can always tell when my deuxjamb is going to feed me. She gets up from in front of the TV-box as soon as the news-news is over and before the sporty comes on.

'I really don't think she likes the sporty, coz when the deuxjambs in the TV-box have sporty first, before the newsy bits, my deuxjamb gets really cranky. She gets all sweary and goes on and on with: *agh! bloody footy! That's not news. Didn't anything important happen in the world today? Bloody footy.*

'Whatever footy is, I don't like it either coz she gets loud.'

'Oh yes, I know what you mean,' I nod, trying not to give away the fact I don't have a clue what he's talking about. 'And please don't call me Fudgie'.

'Okay, cool. And it's sort of the same in the morning,' Humbug continues. 'When the music-clockbox beside her bed suddenly starts talking, which always frightens the itty dutties out of me, she always groans, rolls over, groans again, spreads her legs out – nearly tipping me off the bed – and then flings the bed cover off and jumps out.

'The weird about this is, that even though I know she's going to do this every morning, I am never really prepared for the actual moment. So coz I'm surprised by a thing I know is going to happen, I always let her know that I'm miffed. I give a good yowly and protest a lot to make sure she gives me a hug. So I've got it all figured out really. That's what hyla's all about. Simple.'

Weirdly, Humbug's jabbering starts making sense to me. I get to thinking about some of the predictable things Darling and Hayoo do.

I smile as I think about Hayoo opening the door of the rain room every morning so I can lick her jambs. I know she's going to do that as soon as the rain stops. And every time, she giggles and tells me how strange I am. I love it!

I also know when she's going to get the noisy sucker-dragon out – but that's only because she forewarns me – so I guess it doesn't really count as hyla.

But this is all enough to do my head in; completely. I can't believe I'm umbi to all these clever kisskies. And we haven't found them *all* yet.

'Hey this is fun,' says Raffles, who is still flipping through the file box. 'It tells us everything we need to know – oh, and probably some things we don't – about what the deuxjambs think of us. Here's yours, Big Dan.'

Big Dan peers at the card from the opposite side. 'What?' he exclaims, 'I'm not a fool. It says I'm a fool.'

Raffles cracks up. 'You're reading it upside down, stoopid. It says *aloof*, not *a fool* – ya fool.'

'Oh,' says Big Dan, as he duffs his head.

'What's a loof?' Finny asks.

We all look at each other. Nobody's game to offer a definition.

'Isn't it something deuxjambs use in the rain room?' Humbug asks.

'No, idiot-brain,' the Colonel says, less than politely, 'that's a "loof*a*". I think you'll find that aloof means shy, timid, distant, *reserved* even.'

'Geez, you're a regular thesaurus, aren't you?' Humbug retorts, a bit sarcastically.

'But I'm not,' Big Dan protests. 'I'm not *aloof*, am I?'

'I wouldn't say so,' I remark. 'In fact, not at all. Maybe it's just what Miss Steph thinks. Or maybe she's afraid of you coz you're so big.'

'I doubt it.'

'Well maybe it was a first impression,' the Colonel suggests. 'Maybe she thought you were a bit aloof at first, you know, and now she's got to know you better. Yeah, that's it. I wouldn't be too upset by it, boy.'

'Upset? I don't get upset. Especially not about things like that. If she wants me to be aloof then I'll *be* aloof.'

'I'd like to be nonchalant,' I say, although I think I actually meant to just *think* it. I get the third degree from at least 11 pairs of eyes. 'If I knew how,' I add.

'If you knew *why,*' Maharani says.

I ignore her comment and get to wondering what *my* file card says. I mean Miss Steph's only just met me so she couldn't have come to any conclusions about my personality yet. I reach across the desk and place my paw on the card and slide it towards me but, darn it, Raffles beats me to it. Before I can even open my mouth, he starts reading.

'Comments and observations. This cat is overweight and will be introduced to the KBC program–'

'What's that?' six voices ask in unison.

'Don't know, hang on,' Raffles says, as he rummages through some other paperwork on the desk. 'Oh, this is it,' he says picking up a pamphlet. 'Kitty Boot Camp – a strict diet and exercise regime designed to help your cat shed weight.'

'Ha ha ha.' I'm nearly deafened by the synchronised laughing around the desk.

'Yeah well don't *you* laugh Humbug, because according to this,' Raffles waves Humbug's file card around, 'you're in Boot Camp too'.

'Well that explains a lot,' Humbug says nodding. 'That's why I'm hungry all the time.'

The realisation hits me too. 'I just thought Miss Steph was being a big stingy when in fact she's systematically starving us,' I say to Humbug specifically.

'So we'll show her, Humbug. Let's hit the kitchen,' I declare. I'm barely out of the chair when a big paw catches my shoulder. I turn to find Big Dan's mesmerising green eyes mesmerising *my* green eyes.

'Maybe she's doing this for the sake of your health. Maybe it's at your deuxjambs' request; maybe it's not such a bad idea—'

'Yeah, maybe, maybe, maybe. And maybe I'm hungry. C'mon Humbug. They just don't understand.'

Humbug follows me like a lapquiffo, positively salivating at the prospect of a sneaky feed. As I enter the kitchen, I look up at the shelves around me. Typical, all the interesting stuff is up high. I doubt I can jump as high as the kitzbitz shelf.

'Here, stand just there Humbug,' I point, 'now let me get a bit of a run-up and I'll bounce off your back, up to the shelf.' I have it all worked out. The thought of some extra dinner gets my cathletic adrenalin flowing.

'Why don't you just use the stool?' Humbug suggests.

'Huh? Oh, yeah. Good idea,' I acknowledge.

I jog up the two steps and launch myself up at the shelf, skidding on the slippery white surface and just managing to dig my claws in before I go straight off the other side. I grab one of the shiny bags on the way through. It almost surely contains those delectable little crunchy things which, I now realise, I've been getting stuck-on-a-desert-island rations of. No wonder I was at such a disadvantage playing dizza. I toss the bag down to Humbug who wastes no time trying to figure out how to get into it. Unfortunately, it seems the stuff has been packaged by *Fatcats Incorporated*, rendering it impervious to tampering. I peer down from the shelf and have to quickly lick the corners of my mouth to stop the drool dribbling onto the floor.

'Couldn't you find an open one?' Humbug asks.

Bright feeli this one. I scan the room. 'Down there on that wheelie-table thing; there's a placky thing with a lid.'

Humbug leaps up onto the table and paws the placky thing until it tips over. Something pops and a gush of kitzbitz streams out onto the table and spills over onto the floor.

'Perfect!' I say in mid air as I land on top of the pile. Funny how these little crunchy things taste just like wimbies. We scoff them down like there's no tomorrow until I honestly can't fit even one more in. Well, maybe one more.

'Oh, I think I'm full,' Humbug declares at almost the same moment. 'Think I'll have to sleep it off now,' he yawns.

Of course his yawn makes me yawn. I yawn so wide probably everyone can see the wimby-crunchies I just ate, but I can't help it. I come over all sleepy.

'Umbi, Umbi, quick! Miss Steph's coming.'

I'm sure I'm dreaming, but the prodding on my shoulder and in my face seems pretty real. I open one eye. It's Inda, wide eyed and urgent.

'What, what?' I question.

'C'mon we've gotta get back to our beds,' he cries urgently.

I can hardly move. I try to stand but my legs won't support me. I feel like a drunk bowling ball. I manage to get my front legs to work, but my back ones aren't going anywhere, like one of those flubbery things that hauls itself out of the water onto those white floaty things that Yahoo loves to watch on the TV-box. Inda tries to help; he sort of nuzzles his head under my ooti and pushes me out of the kitchen and towards the feeli quarters, just as I hear the door opening behind us. There's a mad scrabbling as Big Dan, Maharani, Finny and the others jump over me in a frantic dash to their quarters.

'Quick Inda, there's not enough time to get me to my bed. C'mon, we'll just go in yours together.'

'But Umbi–'

'Don't question me, just do it.'

We're no sooner inside when I hear gates clicking all over the place. I turn to see Raffles pushing all the gates closed as he skids down the aisle and dives into his own quarters.

'Phew, that was close,' he calls out. 'Now, everyone act *pussano* or pretend you're asleep.'

Not hard for me, since I still can't move. Inda starts to quirrel and to pronkledonk my belly, then my shoulder, then my belly again. It's soothing, despite his sharpish claws. He curls up against my belly, between my legs and his quirrelling becomes more emphatic. I'm just about nodding off when–

'Huuumbugggggggg, what *are* you doing? How did you get in here? Don't tell me you've eaten all that?'

It's Miss Steph, obviously, and she doesn't sound very impressed. But hey, it gets me off the hook. I can just see her through our doorway, standing in the kitchen with her back to me. She scoops the near comatose Humbug off the table, turns on her heels, and heads towards us through the door.

'Now back into your pen, you naughty boy.' I hear his gate click and I hear him groan as she puts him in his bed. 'What a silly sausage,' she says in a forgiving and soothing tone.

I stifle a giggle. Just as I'm doing so, I become aware of Miss Steph tiptoeing backwards towards Inda's pen. She peers over her shoulder.

'What? How? Who?' she blithers, then her tone gets all accusative. 'Miss Fudgepuddle!' I look sideways, figuring that maybe if I do that she can't see me. I pray for feelichatra but I think I'm probably too relaxed for that.

'How on earth did you get in there? The gate's shut. Are you a magician or something?' she mutters. I don't know what she expects me to say, so I put on my best fuzpah face and say, 'meh?'

Inda stretches and yawns, then puts his head down again and buries it in my chest. I see Miss Steph tip her head to one side. She smiles. 'Oh that's so cute,' she says. 'Do you want to stay there then for a while?'

'Meh.'

'All right.' And she just walks away.

Off with the Queekees

I wake to a kick in the stomach and, with my eyes barely open, I stretch out as far as I can; even stretching my toes in different directions to wake them up. Inda stirs as well, stretching until his foot catches me on the chin. Another kick in the stomach. He looks like a furry rubber band; *my* furry rubber band. He's the longest kisskie I've ever seen. All legs and tail. I quirrel so animatedly that I start to dribble; and when I shake my head, I flick the drool at the walls.

'Oh yuk, Umbi,' Inda says indignantly as he wipes some offending slobber from his face. I lick it off for him and he quirrels, too. I continue up his head and give his ears a good clean. It looks like they haven't been done for a while.

Then I get that disconcerting claws-down-the-kitchen-cupboard-fur-standing-on-end feeling that we're being watched. I swivel my head like Lyn Dablaire in that creepy head-swivelling movie, all the while trying to look nonchalant, and roll my eyes until I fix on the object of my disconcertingment. Miss Steph is standing in the next pen peering at us through the wire. I can't really see what she's doing coz of the wall that goes half-way up but, yep, she's just standing there staring and smiling at us.

'Hello Miss Fudgepuddle,' she coos. 'If only you could talk'.

'I can, silly, I can. And I'd like to introduce you to my dos, Inda.'

'I don't think your owners are going to believe this,' she continues, oblivious to my introduction.

She watches a little longer and then walks off down the aisle, chatting to some of the other guys along the way.

'I can't believe she's just left us here,' I remark.

'It's really good though huh, Umbi? Hoobydoods, hoobydoods.'

'Yes Inda, it's hoobydoods. It's heaven on a fishstick.'

'Huh?'

'Never mind.'

'You know what I mean; those huge ones with the gigantic pink beaks. They live near the sea.' It's Choux-Fleur's voice I hear, sort of distant, like she's outside. I realise that Inda's not curled up with me any more and I wonder how long I've been asleep and what I've missed.

'Oh, you mean Terrorcacktils?' Raffles asks.

'Yeah, that's them. They're frightening with those big mouths that could scoop you up and store you as a delicacy for later on,' Choux-Fleur says.

'I don't really think they're into eating feelis,' the Colonel says soothingly, 'so I wouldn't worry about them. They remind me of Lancaster bombers, especially when they're zooming in to land.'

'Well I still think they're scary. But then so are those noisy white queekees with the yellow hats. They'd peck your eyes out and deafen you at the same time. Such a cackleophony they make.'

'Yes, really arrgarg,' the Colonel agrees.

I realise they're sitting outside their windows; it must be time for queekee-watching. I figure that's as good a way to kill time as any. I stretch a bit and wander up the ramp, onto the top shelf, and stick my head out the window. Inda's already out there, soaking up the late afternoon sunshine.

'Hi guys.' I nod at the Colonel and Choux-Fleur and then realise that Zsa Zsa, Big Dan and Raffles are outside in their runs too.

'What about those black and white things that just hang around and hang around – waiting all the time?' Choux-Fleur asks.

'Yeah, what are they waiting for anyway?' I chime in.

'Dunno, probably a grand final or something.'

'Huh?'

'You have to learn, basically, to just tackle the ones you know you can manage,' Big Dan offers. 'I mean there's no point chasing a Terrorcacktil if you're not big enough or strong enough. They probably *would* carry you away in their big beaky-bag and save you for later.

'Just concentrate on the little ones that hang around the house and remember, if you catch one, you have to take it inside for your deuxjambs' approval. There's no point going to the trouble of catching them if you can't show off your hunting prowess.'

'My deuxjambs always scream at me if I take a queekee inside. They don't seem to appreciate it at all and they especially don't like it if I haven't nuffed it yet,' Choux-Fleur says. 'That's when they *really* roop and run around like quiffos with a bad case of virtles.'

'Yeah, they're not crazy about woozels either,' I put in. 'I've never heard Hayoo squeal so loud as the day I dropped a woozel in her slipper. That was when I discovered deuxjambs threw schpitzos as well.'

'Ooh, ooh, look at that one,' Zsa Zsa blurts, pointing at a foolhardy little queekee which has just landed on the bush next to her.

'That's a Flinch, Zsa Zsa,' the Colonel says. 'Don't bother with them; not enough meat on them. And don't bother with Spattows either – too many bones.'

'And don't try Cookyburrows either, coz when you miss them – and you will – their whole family sits around and laughs at you. It's humiliating,' Raffles says.

'I tried to catch a queekee once,' Inda says, 'but every time I pawed it, it just slipped away. It kept going sideways and disappearing around the corner, then I'd look around the corner and it wasn't there. There was just a whole lot of dust and wobblycobs; and it was hot back there. Then I came out and it was there again, but no matter how hard I tried I just couldn't catch it.'

We all look at Inda; somewhat perplexed.

'Where was this?' Big Dan asks.

'Huh? Oh, inside, at home.'

It dawns on us all at once and we crack up laughing.

'What? What?' Inda asks insistently.

'You'll never catch *those* queekees, lad. They never come out of the TV-box,' Big Dan explains.

'Oh,' Inda says dejectedly.

'We have those irritating Tuk-tuks at our place – they drive me mental,' Choux-Fleur interrupts.

'What are they?' I ask. 'I haven't heard of those.'

'You haven't heard of them? But I bet you've *heard* them.'

'What do you mean?'

'Y'know those obnoxious queekees that go *tuk-tuk-tuk* at you every time you go outside.'

'Oh *those*. Yeah, I *have* heard them. But they're not as annoying as those other grey ones that Hayoo calls phillipbirds.'

'Phillipbirds?'

'Yeah, coz they flit around the trees going: *phillip-phillip, phillip-phillip*. The noise they make is positively arrgarg.'

'Ah them,' the Colonel interjects. 'The ones around our place speak a different dialect, coz they scream, *pheelip, pheelip-pheelip*'.

'Just as annoying, I bet.'

'You bet right, but I know how to shut them up, coz they're pretty thick and slow. They taste good too.'

'I've only ever had one; gave me bloody indigestion,' I recall. 'Oh and there I was trying to shut the darn thing up when its family turned up to see what the racket was. Next thing I know, they're all swooping at me and pecking my back. Nasty experience. Nasty. I swore then and there that Phillipbirds were off the menu forever.'

'I hate those snooty little queekees that dive bomb you and try to pluck your fur out,' Big Dan says. 'They're always going *chat-chat-chat* like they've got something important to say and then, in between, they whistle the same tune over and over. Makes you feel like an inmate at Guano Bay. Honestly they're enough to make your claws curl.'

'Yeah and they never stop wagging their tail around like they're making sure it's still there all the time. They're worse than some quiffos,' Choux-Fleur adds.

'What're they called? I can't remember,' I ask.

'Weeny-teeny-tits, I think,' the Colonel offers. 'No, no, sorry, I think they're Titty-tagwails.'

'Oh yeah, that's right,' Choux-Fleur agrees, 'and they're not much chop to eat either. Very unsatisfying and not worth the effort. I prefer f'narts to queekees or woozels anyway, they've got much more meat on them.'

'Yeah, me too,' Big Dan nods, 'I mean a woozel is just like a horz-doova to me; certainly not a meal in itself. But a f'nart, now you can really get your teeth into a f'nart; they're like three or four woozels in one, but with only one head to deal with.'

'The deuxjambs hate them too,' Raffles says. 'I took an un-nuffed one inside once – coz naturally you've got to tease and taunt it first, I mean it's not fair to not let them fight a bit.

'Anyway, I decided to give it to Deer, that's my deuxjamb, but she went ballistic, *really* ballistic. First she jumped up on the bench and then she screeched and rooped, like one of the Yellow-hat queekees.

'So she's squealing at the f'nart and shouting at me and, meanwhile, the f'nart is skiltering all around the place, poking its head in here and there. Not sure if it was trying to hide from me or get away from Deer's noisy schpitzo. And she's still up on the chair and...' He pauses for breath.

'So what happened? What happened?' Inda asks excitedly.

'Well basically I couldn't stand her loud-crazy any more. I mean I can still hear echoes of it now, if I think about it, so I grabbed the little sucker and took it outside again.'

'So did you eat it?' Inda asks

'Hummph, well actually, I hate to admit it, but when I put it down, the bloody thing ran off quick and disappeared through this tiny hole at the bottom of the fence, never to be seen again. So curse Deer and all her screaming and carrying on. I'd have thought she'd have been really proud of me, but she didn't speak to me for the rest of the day. I never will figure out deuxjambs, never,' Raffles says, shaking his head.

'I can't understand why any of you would lower yourself to catching these icky things, let alone *eating* them,' Zsa Zsa says, her face screwed into a picture of disgust. 'Don't your deuxjambs feed you enough?'

'Of course they do, Zsa Zsa,' Raffles says. 'But where's the fun, or the sport, in eating something that's just put there for you? I mean, we have a duty to teach our deuxjambs how to behave of course, and part of those lessons is to show them how to catch their meals.

'They don't seem to have the vaguest idea. They only know how to bring home stuff in those rustly bags. That food is already nuffed and then they nuff it more by making it very hot. Actually, it really doesn't make sense, coz first they put it in the yellum-box to get it nice and cold and then they spend ages making it so hot they complain about it hurting their mooshes. Waste of time if you ask me. I also can't figure out why they go to all that trouble for themselves and then just open a can or a packet for me. Doesn't make a lot of sense, does it?'

'Not when you put it that way, I suppose,' says Zsa Zsa. 'But then I never get anything from a can or packet, mine always comes straight from the yellum-box.'

I'm not sure whether this is a good thing or not, so I make no comment. But all this talking about food is making me hungry again. I flop on my side in the little tunnelly thing, almost pushing Inda off onto the shelf below, and stretch out a bit to soak up the sun, just so I can dream about dinner in comfort.

Instead, I start to think about my precious kisskies: the cuddly Inda; the happy Arelli; the quirky, oh-let's-be-honest, queer Ori; the stagestruck Erna; and the suspiciously-clairvoyant Sizi. I smile again. But wait a minute! I swivel my head in a sudden realisation. What about Arni? What about Arni?

'What about Arni?' I blurt out loud.

'Huh?' Inda asks.

'What about Arni? We haven't found Arni. We didn't get the chance to doodle him.'

'Oh yeah, that's right,' Inda says, 'the rest of us sort of got sidetracked when you and Humbug went off to feed your faces.'

'Sidetracked? What were you doing?'

Inda drops his eyes and avoids mine.

'Inda?' I say in my most-seriused voice, with a slight inflection on the 'da', so I sound like a deadly-earnest umbi.

'Um, um, well–'

'Inda,' I repeat.

'Okay, okay, so I was showing the guys this great weblike called www.feelipuss.tom.'

'Uh huh – and what's that all about?'

'Well, it's sort of um–'

'Goodness Juno,' the Colonel cuts in, 'it's a Z-rated site, get it?'

'Oh my, you mean you can look at that stuff on the intercat?'

'Yup.' Inda says. 'All sorts of feelis doing all sorts of compromising things. Put it this way, you see lots of legs and tails in positions they wouldn't naturally be. And some of the outfits, well!'

'Oh my dog!' I shake my head in disbelief. 'You're too young for that stuff, Inda!'

'Um, Umbi, it's not like I haven't done it myself. I mean I *am* nine months old you know.'

'Oh pfft. Old before your time, I'd say.'

'Maybe we can get back on the intercat after dinner and try to find something about Arni,' Inda suggests. I think he thinks I don't realise that he's just deliberately changed the subject.

Raffles stretches his neck and pipes in. 'Yeah we can get back on tonight and if we can't find out anything about Arni. I can send an f-mail to Jock the Nose. He might be able to find him.'

'Great idea,' I nod to Raffles, 'thanks for that'.

I put my head down to rest again. All this excitement and realising that I'm just one degree of segregation away from fame and possible fortune is all too much for me really. I just wish I could be so good at something that I'd be famous in my own right. I don't want to have to go through my whole life just gaining some vicarious pleasure from my kisskies' successes. Maybe, maybe…

I know! Origami. I wonder whether it's possible to become a famous origamiist. Mmm. I decide to retire inside and think about it.

Turning Japanese

I sit on my shelf – well, Inda's shelf, actually – and ponder my future. I just can't go through my life like a big fudgy blob. I have to apply myself to something.

I close my eyes and visualise the plushy-red carpet. I'm prancing up it...

No, not prancing: sashaying.

That's me – all a-sashay.

A guard of honour of well-heeled and well-to-do feelis is taking a collective breath and holding out all manner of things for me to autograph as I glide forward.

Ahead I see my precious starlet kisskie, Dacata, and even she's waiting to kiss my paw. I nod to her with that knowing, surreptitious superstar nod, as intrinsic as a Catonic handshake.

Ooh, look. There's even some deuxjambs hovering around behind them, genuflecting to my apparent glory as I parade past with tail held high.

Above the portal to the imposing building, a banner flaps:

43rd International Origami Expo

Sacatmento, Catifornia

Featuring world-renowned exponent

Pussfessor Inki Kazumi

Special guest appearance by new world champion

~ Juno Campbell ~

I'm the star of the show – I can't believe it. And from such humble beginnings. I turn to look behind me and realise that the eight or ten feelis humbly following me are my very own entourage. They all stand to attention as I turn; obviously to avoid upstaging me. I feel like the Queen of Sheepa.

This should make Pussfessor Kazumi feel pretty insignificat; his retinue is only two pointy-faced, blue-eyed, skinny-legged subjects.

The crowd is quite unbelievable and I have to duck occasionally to miss being hit with a barrage of paper floomies dropping out of the sky. It's like a sticky tape parade!

It's obviously quite a big deal, this expo, but strangely I feel right at home. Like it's my birth right to be here. I puff out my chest and suck in my flabby flap as best I can, and nod to the adoring crowd, waving occasionally like that deuxjamb lady with the jewels on her head–

'Umbi! Umbi!' The crowds go roopy with cat-a-calling.

'Hey! Umbi!'

Oh dash, that thought flies out of my head like a flock of queekees flying south as I'm jolted from my reverie by my insistent dossy.

'What's up, Inda?'

'It's nearly dinner time, Umbi, you've been asleep for two hours. Miss Steph's in the kitchen and it smells good. It smells like yummy roast queekee-fowl.'

Oooh. To me it smells a bit like Hayoo and Darling's favourite, Cattucky Fried Queekee-fowl!

'Oh good, I was just thinking about food,' I lie. Then the smell hits me. My nostrils flare to absorb the transcendental wafts from the kitchen. Oops, slobber.

I'd better make room for this. I flop off the shelf onto the ramp and down to the floor and then I see it! A pristine sheet of paper lining our kackapod. I might just have time to whip up another masterpiece before dinner. I stretch a bit to inspire my creative juices and limber up my paws – very important, of course, for an expert origamiist.

I delicately pull the paper out, thankful that Inda hasn't soiled it this afternoon, and set to work, being careful not to dinner-drool on the paper and soggify it. A fold here, a crease there, a corresponding crease on this side, flip it over and turn it back the other way. Crouch and hold one end with my elbow and define the crease with my other paw, twist it around again, hold my mouth in the right position and – voila! It's a, um…

'Hey guys, Red and Mars, what do you call those colourful things Japanese women wear?'

'Um. Hang on; it'll come to us,' they reply. 'A kabana; no, hang on, a kibbutz. No, um we know it starts with k,' they say in unison.

'A kimono,' the Colonel announces knowingly.

'Yep, that's it. Well I've made one; it's not very colourful but.'

'Oh Umbi, that's neat. It's cool. Can you teach *me* how to do that?' Inda asks.

'I would, darling, if I had more paper. We'll have to wait until after dinner and get some more from the office.'

I carefully stand my creation up against the wall. Its symmetry is perfect; ah, the talent. Now, if that doesn't impress Miss Steph! Ooh, maybe she'll give me more for dinner. I'm pretty pleased with myself, so I decide to lick my ooti. I'm so absorbed in the ritual that I hardly notice Miss Steph opening the gate behind me. But I *can* smell the delectable dinner she has for us as she bends down to place two bowls on the shelf.

'Now, Miss Fudgepuddle, don't you eat Coalpit's dinner will you.' It's a request not a question I gather.

'I wouldn't dream of it. What sort of umbi do you think I am, that I'd eat my own kisskie's food?'

She ignores me as usual.

'Oh, look at this,' Miss Steph says as she bends down to pick up my masterpiece. 'It looks like another paper plane. Just what *do* you cats get up to when I'm not here?' She's asking the question directly at me; staring into my eyes.

A kimono, it's a kimono, silly! Oh no, don't screw it up.

I can't watch. I hold my paws over my eyes, nearly overbalancing in the process. I'm waiting to hear the sound of paper getting screwed up...

I'm still waiting. I slowly move one paw, just enough to peer around. She's standing there turning it upside down and back to front; her brow furrowed like a... furrow.

'You know, this looks a bit like, um, what do they call it?'

Success! She actually knows what it is. I can't believe it. Now she must realise how clever I am. Surely, there's got to be more queekee-fowl in this for me. I go all coy.

'Meh.' That's all I can say. 'Meh.'

'Origami, that's it.'

'Meh, meh.'

She shakes her head and gives me a scratch on mine. Ooh, more, more please. She bends down, grabs my cheeks in both hands and blows hot air on my head, making a 'brrrrrrrr' noise as she does it. I go all gooey. And I'd thought only Hamish the Handsome, or maybe Big Dan, could have that affect on me.

I smile a big smile and quirrel as loudly as I can.

'I'll have to tell those silly children of mine to keep their school projects out of here, won't I?'

'Huh? What? But–'

She carefully puts my piece of paper perfection on the shelf and picks me up. Yes, she's got one arm around me and the other under my ooti. Just as well I just washed there. She holds me close to her chest and repeats, 'What a smoochy girl.'

I quirrel so excitedly I dribble all down her hand. She doesn't even flinch.

'Maybe the kids think you've got oriental in you. Japanese bobtail, maybe,' she laughs.

Maybe. Ooh, you mean maybe I might have some pedigree blood in my background? It's possible. It would explain my preference for wimby and my now-obvious innate talent for paper folding. Maybe I could take up ikebana or bonsai as well. I wonder if it's possible that there *is* something special about me after all.

Miss Steph quickly shatters my illusions. 'Not very likely. More like Japanese blobtail,' she laughs.

Oh the ignominy of it all – and just when I was feeling so good about myself. But she gives me a long kiss on the head and another scratch on the neck so I instantly forgive her. She plops me back on the ramp and turns around and picks up Inda who's been sitting there with a big grin on his face. She kisses him on the head and he starts to quirrel, smiling at me all the time.

'Now, just look at the mess you two have made here.' She bends down and picks up our kackapod and disappears for a moment. She returns a moment later with two kackapods. Wow, one each, which of course means two more sheets of paper to paw over. But first things first: dinner, of course.

After polishing off my paw-licking-good queekee-fowl, I give myself an all-over wash; a PFO, I call it – pawpits, face and ooti. I watch Inda, who's doing the same, and remind him to wash behind his ears.

'Okay, ready for some more intercat purrfling now,' I call out to everybody.

'It's okay for you, Miss Garbageguts,' Rocky calls back, 'we're still eating'.

'And Miss Steph's still here,' says Big Dan.

'I certainly hope she is,' Finny calls out from the other end of the room. 'I haven't even got my dinner yet. Smells good though'.

'It was, it was,' I affirm.

'I'm just sharpening my nails while I'm waiting,' Zsa Zsa calls out. 'Oh darn, I've broken another one.'

So I have to wait. I might as well work on another creation. Just because Miss Steph doesn't appreciate it, doesn't mean I'm not going to keep doing it. Deuxjambs are just so self-absorbed sometimes. It just figures she'd think those silly-children of hers were capable of doing origami, but not give my talent a thought.

Hmm, let's think about this. I carefully pull out one of the sheets of paper from the kackapod. It's amazing how I just seem to know how to do this. Inda, licking his paw to give his mouth a good tidy-up, sits above me on the shelf.

'Are you gonna make something else, Umbi?'

'Yep. I'm just trying to decide.'

'Make a woozel or a hibby.'

'Okay, that sounds easy enough.' I carefully fold the paper diagonally, then fold it the opposite way. I pick it up and, sitting on my haunches, I do a bit of this and a bit of that; a fold here, a tuck there, a bit of masterful manipulation with this corner and there it is!

'Wow, Umbi, that's incredible. It looks just like a *real* woozel.'

It just astounds me how clever I am. Such dexterity, such creativity, such brilliance. I'm a natural. I could probably fool a *real* woozel with this.

'Hey, Juno, c'mon we've got the puterbox going again.'

Big Dan is standing in the doorway beckoning to me in that tantalising, titivating way that he does. Inda is already way ahead of me, skidding through the doorway and losing traction on the tiles.

'Hurry, Umbi,' he calls as he disappears around the corner into the office. 'I want to look up Erna again and see what she's up to.'

Sounds good to me. I plonk delicately out of my comfy-tub onto the floor and glide across to the door. I do hate to run coz, though I don't like to admit it, there is the likelihood of tripping over my own swinging flabby-flap. I saunter into the office and find almost everyone is there ahead of me.

Big Dan has very politely saved me a seat in front. I jump up just as Erna's weblike finishes loading. A news flash flickers across the screen:

Dacata confesses: 'I don't know who my fuddy is'

Ms Fanny confesses her deepest secrets on the

David Letterbomb show

'Oh arrgarg,' I wail. 'How embarrassing, now the whole world knows. Uck and I can't stand that Letterbomb bloke. Obnoxious, supercilious, catankerous; the sort of guy you reserve all these big words for.' I cover my eyes in shame. I can't look any more.

'Uh-oh,' Maharani says, 'if you think that's bad–'

'What?' I blubber. I can't look.

'You're not gonna like this.'

I move my paw just enough to glimpse the screen.

Dacata says –

'My umbi is an overweight yellumoholic'

Good grief, has she no shame? 'Okay, enough already. Just wait until I get close enough to have a word in that girl's ear. C'mon let's look at something else now. Hey, can we doodle Origami? I want to get some ideas.'

Inda types it in and we all wait, twiddling our collective toes, while the puterbox cogitates. A long list appears on the screen and I scan down it, not really knowing how to pick one site over any other. Inda scrolls down.

'Hey, wait a minute. Click on that one,' I say, pointing. In a moment a weblike appears and as it loads, my mouth starts to gape and I feel a bit giddy. I can't believe what I'm seeing.

It's all about the annual *International Origami Expo Convention* and there's a big picture of – I can't believe it – Pussfessor Inki Kazumi!

I feel truly faint as I stare at the screen.

'Hey, what's the matter, Fudgepuddle?' Raffles asks. 'Your eyes have gone all whiffle.'

I look at him but can hardly focus. 'Huh? Um, you're not going to believe it, but I just had a dream about this. About the expo and this pussfessor.

'But I dreamed that I was *there* – in Sacatmento. And I was a star; even Dacata was there to congratulate me. But how is that possible? How could I have known about this? I'd never even heard of him before.'

'Maybe you're psychit,' the Colonel suggests.

'Maybe you can see into the future like, like Nostradammit,' Maharani offers.

'Maybe I can. I mean how could I have possibly known this? When is it?' I ask; like I'd have a wimby-out-of-water's hope of being able to go.

'Umm, there you go, March 23 to 26,' Inda says.

'Oh foop! That's next month, like only five weeks away. So much for that then. How would I possibly get there?' I'm crestfallen. I pout. I put on my most miserable face. I stick out my bottom lip and I repeat, 'Oh foop!'

'But but, look,' Inda says excitedly. 'It says here that the

Australian qualifying contest is on March 2nd to 4th. And the winner of that gets to travel free to Sacatmento for the international expo!'

My ears prick up, my lip snaps up, my face brightens up and I nearly chuck… with all the excitement I mean. I look around me and see nods of approval from everyone.

'There's hope for you yet, girl,' Big Dan says, with an affectionate tone to his voice. 'If you can get to the qualifier.'

'Yes, yes, maybe I can.'

'Hey,' Raffles butts in, 'all we've got to do is print this out and leave it on the desk for Miss Steph. That will give her the idea and then she'll pass it on to your deuxjambs and maybe, maybe they'll take you there. Good idea, huh?'

'That is a very good plan,' the Colonel nods.

'Ooh, I wish I could go too,' Maharani says.

'Me too, me too,' Finny agrees.

'Hey, if anyone should go with her, it should be *me*. I am family after all,' Inda reminds us.

'You have a good point there darling, except that, of course, the deuxjambs don't know that.'

'Mmm,' he acknowledges. He scrolls further down. 'It looks like you'd have quite a bit of competition. It says here the Australian champion for four years in a row is an Oriental by the name of Junji Sato.'

'Does that mean he has a black belt in origami?' Finny asks.

'Dunno, probably. Wow, look at that!' Inda points at the screen and everyone takes an audible breath as we stare transfixed. Choux-Fleur tilts her head sideways to try to figure it out.

'It's fantastic but what is it?' Finny asks.

'Beats me. Oh, hang on, it says here it's a Tricerapots. Looks complicated,' Raffles says.

'What's a Tricerapots?' Inda asks.

'Not sure, but I think I saw one in the back

yard once. Do you think you could make that Tricerapots?'
Big Dan asks me.

'I reckon I could. Here, pass me some of that paper over.'

Raffles slips me a piece of paper from the tray beside him.
I grab it with both paws, shut my eyes and start. I ignore the
titters and 'ahs' going on around me and bend and fold like
it's second nature to me. It takes a bit longer than the wimby
or the kimono but before long I'm proudly holding out a perfect
orange Tricerapots. Whatever that is.

'Wow!' Raffles says, 'I was timing that. Fifty-two seconds,
that's amazing. This Sato guy here says that his took about
twenty minutes to make.' Raffles shakes his head in disbelief.

'You are amazing, you're a star, Fudgepuddle; er, ah, sorry,
Juno.'

Suddenly I'm surrounded by clapping – which for feelis,
is more of a sight thing than a sound thing – and everyone is
patting me on the back and nodding. And, I can't believe it,
Big Dan is even bowing to me like I'm royalty, or a queen
something.

'You absolutely *have* to get yourself to this contest, Juno,'
the Colonel says. 'You'll be the talk of the origami world.
Who knows, you might even be able to topple that Sato guy
and that Pussfessor Kazumi off their perches. I can see it
now...'

He adopts his most eloquent voice and waves his paws
expansively and says: 'Introducing the new star of origamidom,
the quickest, cleverest and most dexterous new talent in many
a long year – the incredible Juno!

'Just wait until you tell them all how you discovered your
talent; while taking a grunty in your kackapod,' he laughs.
'As Catfucius once say: *Feeli who master kackapod paper go
on to rule Japan!*'

'Did he really say that?' Finny asks.

'Well, words to that effect,' the Colonel replies.

Red and Mars chime in, 'We think you'll find that Catfucius

was Chinese, not Japanese. But nevertheless, we both think you should go for it.'

'I don't know,' I say, 'knowing my luck I'd be beaten by a folding chair.'

So, I'm sitting back in my, sorry, *our* pen, surrounded by folded paper objects of all kinds. Inda's urging me on: 'make this, make that, make a boffle, make a floomy, make a keckoo'.

Honestly, I tell him, if I fold any faster I'll be perforated. But, it seems, that with an endless supply of paper, especially this pretty coloured stuff Raffles found on the shelf in the office, there's nothing I can't create. I'm just a paper-folding freak. It's almost like someone else is controlling my paws. I can even do it in the dark! And now I'm starting to wonder whether there really *is* something in this clairvoyanty stuff. Maybe Sizi got her talent from me, without me even knowing I had it. Wow. Maybe I'm a clairvoyant origamiist. I grin a big grin.

'Umbi, what *are* you doing?'

'Huh? Oh, nothing, Inda-mine, nothing really. I was just having a Zen moment.'

Of flame and gory

Click, flash, click flash!

'I've just been taking some pictures of your wonderful creations, Miss Fudgepuddle,' Miss Steph says.

'Meh?' I think she's beginning to understand me now and she seems really impressed. It looks like Raffles might have had the right idea leaving the notice on the desk for Miss Steph. She must be getting a pawtfolio together to show Hayoo and Darling when they come to get me. Ooh, it's so exciting; I'm going to be famous, I just know it.

'I'd like to see you in action,' Miss Steph says as she turns and heads out of the pen towards the office.

She soon returns with some coloured paper and puts a green piece down in front of me. I look at it waiting for some inspiration.

A hibby, that's it! Hibbies are often green of course.

I pick up the paper with one paw and set to work, looking up occasionally at Miss Steph, who's just standing there looking moosh-thwacked. She raises her eyebrows every now and then and shakes her head. I keep folding the paper back on itself, then around that way and this way until I've formed a perfect hibby. I drop it on the ramp in front of me and place my paw gently on its back. It hops forward, just like a real hibby. Miss Steph gasps, gapes and covers her mouth.

'Oh Fudgepuddle, that's brilliant. Just brilliant. I've never seen anything like it.' She keeps shaking her head, while Inda bats his paws together in applause.

'This has really got to be seen to be believed,' she goes on. 'A cat doing origami; it's incredible! Nobody would believe me if they didn't see it with their own eyes. This is, like, a world first I'm sure; but the world's got to see this. I know what I'll do, I'll ring *Sixty Mittens*. You could be really famous!'

'Wow,' I shake my head in disbelief. 'She's very impressed I think,' I say to Inda.

'So she should be, Umbi, I mean I've never come across anyone else who can do origami. Come to think of it, I've never come across anyone who can do *anything* as quick and perfect as you can. You're a legend, Umbi.'

I've never felt so proud. Finally I think I know what I was put on this earth for. My own kisskie thinks I'm a legend. What more could an umbi want but to bask in her own flame and gory?

I grin really wide and start to roll over a bit, then I have this sudden sensation of falling. I stick my legs out straight in an involuntary spasm and–

Suddenly I'm awake.

Oh, foop! Was I dreaming again?

I open my eyes blearily and nearly jump out of my skin. Miss Steph's standing there with her little camera, clicking away. So that explains the flashes. I must have seen them in my mindmove. And there I was thinking she'd found my origami masterpieces.

Inda is still lying along my belly; his head tucked in under my chin.

'What?' I ask Miss Steph.

'Oh, that's so cute. Look at the two of you. You're obviously meant to be together.' She says to herself. She clicks again, right in my face this time. I blink at the flash.

'Well good morning to you Miss Fudgepuddle,' she addresses me personal this time. 'I hope you don't mind that I just clicked off a couple of pictures of you and Coalpit snuggled up there. You look so cute, I'm sure your owners would love to see this. I'm hoping they won't be able to resist taking Coalpit home with them too, when they come for you.'

She pats me on the head, tickles behind my ears, and does that hot, breathy snuffly thing between my ears again. I go all gooey, I can't help it. I roll into a demi-ipwod and then stretch further into a full ipwod. She rubs my tummy and, oh oh, I start to dribble. She gives Inda a pat too as he stretches and jumps down off the shelf.

'Now, what's all this mess here girl?'

Ooh, ooh, she's checking out the origami. Maybe now she'll realise how clever I am. But no, she swipes her hand across the shelf and knocks all my creations onto the floor. She kicks the keckoo and the floomy and the tricerapots into the corner.

They're all crushed and crumpled into meaningless wads like the ones Hayoo throws around in her office.

Is she blind? Is she stupid? Huh? My illusions are shattered. I much preferred the dream version. How could she? I shake my head in disbelief.

'Now, some breakfast for you two? And then you can have a bit of a wander around out here,' Miss Steph says.

My disappointment at her flagrant ignorance is instantly forgotten at the mention of food. I lick my lips. This deuxjamb mightn't be big on origami but she really knows how to push the right buttons with me.

The only other thing she doesn't seem to know about is my craving for Vegemice. Hayoo often lets me lick it off her finger or puts a dab on my paw. It's just the most delectable stuff; I could eat it all day so long as I have some yellum to wash it down with. Miss Steph also doesn't know about hardyellum; that's something else I miss about being at home. I most like the really tasty one, but the softer one in the silver-foily is pretty delicious too. But I guess kitzbitz definitely have their place in my diet, especially when I know that's all I'm going to get this morning.

Inda and I have a good stretch and inspect our bowls. Mmm, a different flavour today.

'Oh this is yum,' Inda comments between mouthfuls.

'Mmm, not as good as Vegemice though.'

'What's that? I don't think I've ever had that.'

'You would remember if you had. It's black and sticky and salty and–' Uh-oh, salivating again. 'My deuxjambs have it on their burnt bread in the mornings.'

'Mine don't. They have this horrible brown sticky, lumpy stuff that sticks to the roof of your mouth. I only tried it once; it made my whiskers curl and I nearly choked on it. Awful stuff.'

'Maybe you're allergic to it.'

'Yeah, maybe. Anyway, I'll never try it again.'

'Oh, by the way,' I put my paw on Inda's shoulder, 'you might want to save some of that in case we decide to play dizza later.'

'Huh?'

'Never mind, just don't eat it all at once.'

'Hey Umbi, who was that gorgeous feeli who sang to me? I haven't been introduced properly.'

'Oh, that's Finny, she's a sweetie.'

'I never got to hear the end of the song coz you interrupted her when you realised I was me. Y'know I think I could sing, if someone taught me how. Do you think she'd give me some lessons?'

'I'm sure she would, darling, if you ask her nicely.'

'Ooh hoobydoods, hoobydoods,' he says excitedly.

I suspect he maybe has an ulterior motive, but then if *I* were a good-looking young lad, I would probably be smitten by the likes of Finny too.

It's only now that I realise our gate is still open and I remember Miss Steph saying we could have a wander around out there. So she's actually given us permission to socialise with the others, which is good coz I'm missing a lot of the gossip down this end of the place.

'C'mon Inda, I'll take you down and introduce you to Finny properly.'

It's obvious he can barely contain his excitement as he starts jigging and dancing around in circles like Gene Katty. He follows me out of the pen and we saunter importantly down the room, flicking our tails in unison and giving a nod to everyone as we pass their spots.

'This is obviously a reward or prize for my cleverness,' I gloat.

'Hmmph, she thinks her grunties don't stink now,' says Zsa Zsa, as we pass by.

'Do you think we should tell her that we *all* get some time out of our pens at least every other day while Miss Steph's in here cleaning?' Maharani whispers.

Urrgh, she's so good at spoiling the moment. I pretend I didn't hear her.

'Here we are, darling,' I say as we approach Finny's pen.

'Hi Finny, Inda-mine would very much like to ask you something.'

'Hi Inda,' Finny says, fluttering her tail and batting her eyelids. 'What do you want to ask me?'

Inda suddenly goes all coy; an art he's obviously learned from me. 'I, I um–'

'He wants to know if you might give him some singing lessons. I think he thinks he could give Elvis Pussley or Pavacatti a run for their money.'

'Well, every aspiring young singer thinks

they're going to be the next Justin Berber. Does he have a strong, deep voice?'

'I don't know, I've never heard him. Inda?'

He shrugs. 'I don't know, I've never tried'.

'Eeeeeeee,' Finny sings in the deepest tone she can muster. 'There, try that, Inda.'

'Eeeeeeeeeeeeeee,' he squeals.

We all quickly cover our ears with our paws. Maharani pulls a constipated face.

'Definitely not a baritone then,' Finny observes, 'but not a soprano either, thankfully. Maybe a tenor or counter tenor. Now try this, Inda. La la la la la la.' Her voice goes up and down like a wave. Inda follows suit, but at a slightly lower pitch than Finny.

'Mmm, good vibrato and resonation and maybe a touch of coloratura which could be enhanced and developed. Seems he's got a good chest too and good lungs; there might just be some promise.'

I have no idea what she's talking about and, looking at Inda, I presume he doesn't either, but he hasn't taken his eyes off her for a second.

'So will you take him on?' I ask.

'Oh, for sure. We'll have to do it tonight though, coz it will be difficult with him being so far down the end. We could start with something simple, like a nursery rhyme, just to test his ability to follow a tune and remember the words. Maybe something like this.' She clears her throat and begins:

Oh Senor Don Gato was a cat!
On a high red roof Don Gato sat
He went there to read a letter
Miaow miaow miaow
Where the reading light was better
Miaow miaow miaow
'Twas a love note for Don Gato. .

'Oh, that's cute. Is there more? I'd love to hear the rest of it,' Inda blurts.

'Tonight, honey, tonight,' Finny coos.

I'm starting to wonder whether Finny's as smitten with my Inda as he seems to be with her. Maybe they could make wonderful music together; that's if Inda can actually sing. We'll have to wait and see or listen.

'Thanks Finny,' I say and with a gentle nudge I steer Inda further down the building. 'Let's go and visit some of the other guys.

'Hi Beethoven,' I wave. 'Hi Raffles, hi Maharani, hi Colonel, hi Lara.' Inda acknowledges everyone with a nod. 'Hello, Big Dan,' I quirrel in my best erotipuss voice.

'Morning, Miss Juno.' He winks at me.

I swear to God he winked at me!

'Are you enjoying your little outing?' he asks.

'Prrrr yes.'

'You know, we're all quite impressed with your origami. I think you'd have a really good chance if you could get to the competition. Just don't forget us when you become rich and famous.'

'I hear what you're saying, Dan, but I don't think I'd be any different if I were famous.'

'Ha, just look at your own jes,' Zsa Zsa butts in. 'A little bit of celebricat and she's already trying to disown you. Do you think fame hasn't changed her?

'My own umbi and fuddy were the same; quite humble feelis until they became famous. And then they just started to look down their whiskers at everybody else.'

'What, like you?' Maharani says sarcastically.

Zsa Zsa chooses to ignore her, flicking her tail with irritation as she inspects her nails.

'Oh, darn it,' she says, 'I've broken another one'.

'Hey, why not let me *get* famous before you

worry about how I'm going to deal with it? I don't know, everybody's gotta put their two woozels worth in.'

I've still got to figure out how I'm going to even get to the contest, let alone think about how I might or might not cope with the fame that is almost certain to follow if I do.

Inda and I saunter back to our pen to contemplate how we're going to fill in the rest of the day.

He decides to give himself a PFO, while I finish my breakfast. I remember to leave a few kitzbitz, either for Dizza or just for later on, and then climb up to look out the window.

I start to ponder my future. If I become famous, I could have tuna or roast queekee-fowl every night, lashings of yellum in a big bowl every day, a veritable wardrobe full of diamante chokey-straps (to outdo Zsa Zsa) and maybe even my very own armchair-cum-scratcher in front of the fire.

I might even get to travel the world. I could go to London to visit the Queen (whatever that means), I could go to Spain to meet that handsome Don Gato, I could go to Paris to be gay (I've heard that's what they do in Paris).

And when I'm in Americat for the origami expo, I could go to Catalina Island, visit the *real* AlCatraz, maybe go north to see the Catskill Mountains and then go south to Mexico and Catapulco. I could try my luck at catching Speedy Gonzalez while I'm there – *arriba*!

I could go even further south to Purru and see Lake Titicatcat. Ooh, I could go to Italy where I'd be sure to visit Catania and Catanzaro and I could skip across to Morocco and check out Catablanca.

Hmmp. My travel plans are interrupted by a red car coming into the carpark.

'Hoo hoo, red car, red car!' I call out. 'Anyone's deuxjambs have a red car?' I get no answer.

Except then I hear a soft 'uh oh'. I look around and down to the floor. Inda has a glum look on his face.

'Do you think it's my deuxjambs?' he asks, a hint of despair in his voice.

'I don't know, dear, what do they look like?'

'She's got yellum-coloured hair, although not always, and he's got scratchy fur on his face.'

I look out the window as the red car opens. Inda couldn't have given a more accurate description of those deuxjambs if he'd been looking out my window too.

The deuxjambs make their way up the path to the front door. She looks very grumpy and distracted.

Oh dear, just when everything was going along so nicely. Poor Inda is even going to miss out on his singing lessons. I can feel my heart-throbs tearing. Just when my darling Inda and I were getting to know each other so well.

'Sorry Inda-mine, it looks like it might be time for you to go.'

'Oh but I don't *want* to go, Umbi. I want to stay here with you. Can't I?'

'I wish it were that simple, darling. But maybe we can visit from time to time now, since we know where each other lives.'

'It's not quite the same though, is it?'

'No, it's not,' I agree. I dop him with my head and lick his ears and face, quirrelling as loud as any umbi possibly can.

We wait for what seems like caternity. Miss Steph and Inda's deuxjambs must be deep in conversation. We can hear their murmurs and, if my ears serve me correctly, I can hear some sniffing and snuffling. Ooh, ooh, they're coming.

'... to believe this, but just look at the two of them,' Miss Steph says as she enters the big room. 'They've really taken to each other'.

'Wait a minute,' the lady deuxjamb says. 'That cat actually looks like Coalpit's mother. Remember darling? His mother was a big flabby

139

white and ginger cat, just like that one. Maybe it is, maybe that's why they seem to be getting along so well.'

'Hmm, whatever,' the man deuxjamb says.

'Campbell, is her surname Campbell?' the lady deuxjamb asks Miss Steph.

'Yes, yes it is. Ooh, you might be right.'

'Well I never. So do you think there's any chance that they might have Coalpit back? That would solve our problem.'

'Huh?' Coalpit says.

'Huh?' I say.

'Well, the best thing I can do is wait for the Campbells to get back and ask them. If you're sure you can't take him, I'll see if I can convince them. They are lovely people so I'm sure if they saw the two of them together, they wouldn't be able to resist taking Coalpit too.'

'Good, and maybe they'll give me a new name too,' Inda says smartly.

Then, changing his tone, he says to me, 'I think they don't want me any more, Umbi'. His bottom lip starts to curl and I can see a tear welling in his right eye.

'I think you might be right. But you said you weren't all that happy there anyway. Just you wait until Darling and Hayoo come back to get me. We'll put on the most pathetic pussano display they've ever seen and there'll be no way they'll leave you behind. Then we can be together all the time.'

'Ooh, hoobydoods, hoobydoods.'

The prisoner of afaQsban

'I do have to have one last hug. I mean I can't just leave him behind without saying goodbye,' Inda's lady deuxjamb says in a toffee voice.

Gee, what a magnanimous gesture.

She steps into our pen and bends down to pick up Inda.

'Psst,' I whisper, 'looks like a good time for a schpitzo, dossy.'

And, as he's being lifted into the air, he winks at me.

Before I know it, all hell breaks loose; which is worth seeing in such a confined space.

Inda yarls deafeningly and runs up the she-deuxjamb's arm and, in a grey blur which looks like the linty trap in the turmble-dryer, launches himself off her shoulder, over my head, onto the shelf, and out the window.

She screams, coz he's left scratch marks all up her arm. Oh, and it appears she's broken a fingernail. The he-deuxjamb is jumping up and down grunting and holding his foot coz the lady deuxjamb has stepped on it.

Then Miss Steph lets out a roop because she and he have

banged heads while she's bending down to help him. I cop an elbow in the face as the she-deuxjamb swings around to try to catch Inda, who by now, of course, has disappeared out of sight.

I shake my head to try to get my eyes to stop wobbling from the clobbering, and feel like I'm in a Garfield catoon.

All this and everyone else is cheering in the background.

'Yeah, you tell 'er,' Humbug calls out.

'She doesn't deserve you,' Raffles says.

'Bite her, bite her,' Maharani squeals.

'Give her what for,' the Colonel says imperiously.

'Come on you lot, calm down,' Big Dan admonishes.

'Okay, I get the message,' the she-deuxjamb calls out the window. Then she turns to address Miss Steph. 'He always was a horrid, snarly little creature.'

'Oh really?' I say.

'Oh really?' Miss Steph says at the *very same* time. I swear sometimes she must understand what I say, either that or I can telegraph my thoughts, um, telegraphically.

'I've found him to be a delightful little thing, she is saying. 'Not a cross word at all – in fact he's very purry and affectionate.'

I do believe Miss Steph is trying to rub it in now.

'Hmmp,' the she-deuxjamb says as she turns on her heels and heads for the door.

'Well good riddance to you,' I call out.

'Yeah, scram,' Raffles adds for effect.

Inda pops his head back in the window. 'And don't come back, pttthhhh.' He jumps down the ramp towards me and we dop heads again. He's so happy he puts his paw up to give me five – but, at almost the same moment, his eyes widen as though someone's trodden on his tail.

'Oh, no,' he gasps. 'But if I come to live with you, I won't see Arelli any more and she won't know what's happened to me. I didn't think of that.'

'How far away do you think you live from each other?' Big Dan asks. 'Because now we know where Juno lives and you know where you live, that means you'd both know where Arelli lives,' he suggests.

'Gee, he's right, Umbi,' Inda nods.

'Huh? I'm confused,' I admit.

'Well, if I know where *I* live and you know where *you* live, all we have to do is figure out how to get from *your* place, which is now my *new* place, to my *old* place and then you can get to see Arelli too, coz she's just down the road. Get it?'

'Oh yes, I see.' Not.

'That's where you need a GPS,' Raffles calls out.

'What's that?' I ask dumbly.

'D'oh Umbi, it's a Global Pussycat Searcher!'

'Well how was I to know that? I've never had one.'

'All we'd have to do when we get home to your place is type in my old place and it'll show us how to get there. It'll give us the distance and the most direct route and even a rough traveling time; well, for if you're in a car, anyway.'

'But I don't have one and nor do Darling and Hayoo as far as I know.'

'It'd be in their car if they do, somewhere up near the bug-squash glass,' Raffles says.

'Nope, I'm pretty sure they haven't got one of those.'

'So, you might need a map then,' Raffles suggests. 'I tell you what; Miss Steph has a map in her office, up on the wall. We can check it out later.'

'Good idea, Raff,' I nod. Then it occurs to me; like a light of boltning. We could find Ori and Sizi the same way. We already know Ori's address and maybe we just have to send Sizi an fmail to get hers and we could have a real reunion, with all the family. Except of course for Erna who's not likely to be able to get here from Hollypudd on the Gold Coast.

Or Arni; my dear, elusive Arni. Hang on. Maybe Ori or Sizi might know where Arni is.

That's a thought. I keep having these brilliant thoughts. Why didn't we all think of fmailing Sizi before? Sizi should know where Arni-mine is, if she really *is* sceptic; um psychit.

It's a pity it's still a few hours until night because I can see it's going to be a busy one: Inda's first singing lesson, a bit more intercat purrfling, maybe finding Arni and goodness knows what else is in store.

I feel I should get myself prepared for it. A serious PFO is in order; in fact a CAT (cleanse allover treatment) is the go. The only trouble with this, of course, is that one has to get oneself into all manner of awkward positions. I mean licking your own back isn't something everyone can do; licking your elbows is especially tricky; and licking your own ooti is not as satisfying as some might think.

And, for some reason, it all seems much more difficult for me than it used to be. I think maybe my tongue has shrunk. Or maybe elbows just get further away the older you get. Who knows? Anyway, I'm going to spend some time this afternoon giving myself the full treatment from my ears to my ooti and beyond to the tip of my tail. Then I'll have a nice long nap so I'll be perfectly fresh for the evening's events.

'Incoming, incoming,' Rabbit yells.

Rrrrr, why is it that every time I'm comfortable napping, somebody or something wakes me up? I stretch a bit and crane my head toward the window to see what or who Raffles is going on about. There's a yellow car in the car park, but I've just missed seeing the deuxjamb.

'It's not your deuxjambs, is it?' Inda asks.

'No darling, mine have a silver car. Besides I'm not – or hopefully *we're* not – going until Thursday. Actually, I wish it was them, because I can't wait to get home again. I have my own window in the sun, my own place in bed with Hayoo, my own kackapod, my own everything.'

145

'But what about me? Won't you share all this with me?'

I confess I hadn't thought about that. I really hadn't. What if he gets bigger and hogs the bed? What if he eats all my food and drinks my yellum when I'm not watching? What if he finds all my hidey spots?

I'll just have to keep him in line, that's all. I am the boss, after all. I'm the *umbi* in this equation. So no problem. I hope.

Miss Steph walks in with a carrier in her hand and a pair of youngish deuxjambs – one of each kind – behind her.

I get a quick glimpse of the new inmate – looks like one of those three-coloured turtlenecks – as everyone starts calling out and welcoming the new arrival. The Colonel, Raffles, Big Dan, Maharani and Zsa Zsa all call out their names like a second-grade roll call.

'Now I'm sure these surroundings are much more salubrious than where you've come from,' Miss Steph says. The deuxjambs seem to agree.

'Yes, I mean the pound is clean enough,' the lady deuxjamb says, 'but they sure are jammed in like sardines there. There's not nearly as much space as here. It's just a pity that it's taken us this long to find the perfect cat there; right when we're going on holidays.'

'Don't worry about that. I'll take good care of her. This might be a good transition for her anyway. She can socialise a bit with some of the other cats and should be very friendly and relaxed by the time you come back for her. Now, I'll pop her in number 27 here. I'm sure she'll be comfortable. Won't you, gorgeous?' Miss Steph says soothingly.

'She's lucky they've brought her here instead of AlCATraz,' the Colonel remarks. 'That obviously means her new deuxjambs have good taste.'

The new arrival goes through the usual fussing and fluffing of being settled in but, despite all our welcomes, we haven't heard a peep out of her yet. Maybe she's waiting until the deuxjambs have gone.

'Hey, you, what's your name?' Maharani whispers. 'I'm Maharani Shani, but you can just call me Maharani. My deuxjambs call me Taya, though.'

'Hi, Maharani, my name is Purdy, but I'm not sure what my new deuxjambs are planning to call me yet. They've been going through all number or freaky possibilities in the car on the way here. Things like Blossom and Fairy and Agatha, yuck. I've just been adopted if you haven't figured that out already.'

'So why were you at the AFAQS?' Raffles asks. 'Did you run away from home?'

'No, I would never have done that. I loved my deuxjamb and she loved me, but she was very sick. I stayed right by her side to the very end, before the noisy deuxjambs came and took her away to Weeras on a rolling bed,' she sniffs.

'Oh,' Raffles says, and makes no further comment.

'So how did you end up at the AFAQS?' I ask.

'My deuxjamb's friend, who used to mind me from time to time, took me there to find me a new home.'

'Oh, so how long were you there? Were there many other feelis there? What was it like?' I ask.

'I was there about nine or ten days, but it seemed like much longer because it was sooooooo yawny. There's just nothing to do and everyone is so anxious about whether their own deuxjambs are coming back for them, or whether some other nice deuxjambs will take them home or whether they're going to be sent to Weeras or what's going to happen. So nobody talks much; they're certainly not as friendly there as you lot seem to be.'

'It sounds positively awful,' I say.

'Well, it's not *that* bad; I mean most of the feelis do get to go to either their old home or a new home. But then, of course there's the ones that aren't very pleasant or very pretty, or maybe they're just really old, and nobody wants to take them home.'

'So what happens to them?' I ask.

147

'Well usually they're only there for a few days and then a deuxjamb, one of the ones we see regularly, comes and takes them away and we don't see them again. They're usually kept down the other end of the building; the spot everyone calls Weeras Way.'

'Oh,' I gasp, 'so they go to Weeras?'

'Yes, or worse,' Purdy says.

'Oh gosh, I hope *I* never end up there. So how many feelis were there; in Weeras Way I mean?'

'Hmm,' Purdy thinks, 'three when I arrived, but only one when I left the day before yesterday. He's been stuck in there for at least two weeks. Nobody seems to want him, I guess because he's so big and hairy. He was a great big brute. I could just get a glimpse of him if the door was open and he came to the front of his pen while I was at the front of mine.'

'So what did he look like?' I ask, not really knowing why I'm so curious.

'As I said, biiig with glowering green eyes, long shaggy grey fur and a big bushy tail. He was very well spoken though; like he'd been well brought up,' Purdy explains.

My fur frickles a bit, I lick my lips and I swish my tail; thinking, imagining, hoping it's not–

'I think his name was Hamish,' Purdy says.

'*Hamish*?' I gasp.

'Yeah, Hamish, or Horace or Humphrey. Something like that.'

'Oh god, my Hamish! My Hamish the Handsome in Weeras Way. What's happened?' I panic and bolt for my gate. 'Silly fool. How did he end up at the AFAQS? And what if–'

I throw myself at the gate and rattle it. 'I've got to get out of here, I've got to go and rescue my Hamish.'

I rattle the gate as hard as I can; so loudly that I only barely hear Big Dan's words.

'Juno, Juno, calm down, girl. You can't do anything from in here.'

'I know, I know,' I schpiff, 'that's why I've gotta get out of here. Otherwise it'll be too late.'

'Umbi, Umbi, who's Hamish?' Inda asks me, prodding me on the back elbows. 'What's the matter?'

'Never mind dossy, I can't explain now. I just know that I'll never forgive myself if I don't help him. But what can I do from here?'

'Would you even know where to go, if you *weren't* in here?' the Colonel asks.

'I'd find a GSP and look it up.'

'GPS,' the Colonel corrects.

'Yeah, one of those. I'd look it up and go there and rescue him.'

'I hate to kill your enthusiasm,' Big Dan utters, 'but I don't think it would be quite so easy. You'd need help for starters. And what if you got caught? You'd end up in there, too, and your deuxjambs wouldn't be very pleased. I think you need to calm down and think this through. I mean, even if you could get out of your pen now, have you thought about how you're going to get out of the building and then find your way to the AFAQS from here?'

I plonk my ooti on the ground. Defeated. He's right, I know he's right. But I've *got* to do something. I can't just leave my Hamish honey there and not try to help. Inda does figure eights around my legs to comfort me. He realises I'm upset even if he's not sure why. One day I'll tell him, but not right now.

I can't wait until Thursday to get out of here – that's still three days away. It might be too late by then. I have to come up with a plan. I mean if I could rescue Hamish, he'd be indebted to me forever. I could make him my own personal toy boy and I could be his sex kitten – or cougar more like it.

Oh stop it! Think straight, girl. What are you going to do? I ask myself but I'm not getting any answers. Too much to think about at once. I'd like to be able to be like Starlet O'Hara in *Gone*

out the Window, and just think about it tomorrow, but I have to think about it now.

'Eeeoww,' I yarl, 'I need help. Colonel, surely with your military expertise you can help plan a strategy, and Raffles, little Mister Escapologist, you can surely figure a way out of here.'

'We'll put our heads together and work on it,' the Colonel says.

'Yeah, don't worry Juno, we'll come up with a plan. Mind you, I don't think you'll want to wait for the Colonel to hatch an escape plan, you could be waiting until the cows come home – which they never seem to do. At least they don't ever come home to our place,' Raffles says.

I start to relax a bit. But it's pretty frustrating now, being stuck in here when everything else seems to be happening Out There!

Hamish is out there, probably on his way to Weeras; my Arni is out there, somewhere, waiting for me to find him; my future as an origamiist can only happen out there; my Erna is way up there; Hayoo and Darling are goodness-knows-where.

And where am I? *I* am stuck in here, that's where I am; twiddling my whiskers.

I'm really starting to wish that Darling and Hayoo would hurry up and come back so that Inda and I could just get home and figure out what we're going to do about everything. Honestly, if I have to wait for the Colonel to figure out a plan, I'll be old and grey and Hamish the Handsome will have gone to Weeras – or *beyond*. I can't see how we can possibly get out of here and find the AFAQS and bust Hamish out. Looks like I'll just have to wait until I get home and then work out a plan and hope it's not too late for Hamish.

But then I remember something that's going to put a spanner in the wok: Darling and Hayoo always keep me inside for the first two or three days after I get home from my holidays. Why they do that I have *no* idea. It's not like I'm going to want to run back to the other theres I was sent – especially not when I've just got home. And, oh dear, if they do take Inda home as well, it's probably even more likely they'll keep us both shut in for ages.

So if they shut me in this time, how will I get away to save my Hamish? Oh, what am I going to do? If only these stupid deuxjambs could understand me when I speak to them. You'd think that if they've figured out how to fly to the moony, how to build skyscratchers and how to operate mote-controls, they'd have figured out feeli-speak by now. It's obvious they're going to be no use to me as I won't be able to explain the urgency of the situation to them. Somehow, I've got to get to the AFAQS by myself to rescue Hamish. Maybe I'll get have to get away and get lost myself – ah! There's a thought…

'I've got it guys! I've just got to get lost and I'll be picked up by the green-shirt deuxjambs and taken to the AFAQS. Then I'll be able to rescue Hamish.'

That's it: that's my plan. I feel pretty smug now with this brilliant idea.

'Mmm,' says the Colonel, 'but how are *you* going to get *him* out if you're stuck in there too? Did you think about that?'

'Um, Raffles will have to come too so that he can figure a way out.'

'Sounds logical to me,' Raffles says, 'except that I'm stuck in here for another two weeks or so yet. And anyway, what interest do *I* have in getting this Hamish out? It's not like I know him or anything.'

'Yeah, point taken. But you'd really like him, Raffles, I know you would. It would be like your good deed for the month, and he'd be forever indebted to you.'

'Okay, well my suggestion is: we wait until tonight so that we can get the map from Miss Steph's office, then we figure out how to get out of here. Maybe I'll be able to figure out how to get a door or window open, then we go lickety-split to the AFAQS and then, um, we just hang around outside there until the morning when someone's bound to pick us up and take us inside.'

'Oh Raffles, that's brilliant. That'll work, don't you reckon, Colonel? Big Dan?'

'It sounds like a feasible plan to me,' the Colonel says.

'I think it could work, Juno,' Big Dan agrees, 'but if you're going to do it, I think I should come too just to be sure that nothing bad happens to you two. I could just imagine you'd be like a pair of loose catapults, going off all over the place. You'll need somebody to keep an eye on you.'

'Okay, that'd be neat, Big Dan,' I nod thoughtfully. 'And I'd feel much safer with you there.'

'Then it's a plan,' Big Dan says. 'But something tells me our deuxjambs and Miss Steph aren't going to be too impressed about this.'

'No, I should think not,' Zsa Zsa adds, condescendly.

'And your deuxjambs aren't going to be too impressed with Miss Steph if you lot bust out of here either,' Maharani says.

Oh. I hadn't thought of that. I mean, I wouldn't want Miss Steph to think I didn't like it here. After all, this is the best place I've ever been – other than home, of course.

'Hang on! I've got a better idea,' I say.

'What?' Big Dan, Raffles and the Colonel ask in unison.

'Why don't we break into the AFAQS tonight, bust Hamish out and be back here in our pens by morning? That way, Miss Steph will never know we've been anywhere, we won't get stuck in there and our deuxjambs won't have to pay big kitzbitz to get us out of there. If we leave here as soon as it's dark enough, we'll have a good eight or ten hours to find our way there, figure out how to get in and rescue Hamish, and get back here again.'

'We can certainly give it a try,' Raffles says. 'It will depend on whether we can find a way to get Hamish out. But hey, as I said, they don't call me Houdini for nothing.'

'Yes, but Houdini was famous for getting *out* of things – not getting *into* things,' Zsa Zsa points out.

'In-out, whatever,' Raffles retorts. 'So after dusk then?'

'Yep, as soon as Miss Steph tucks us in for the night.'

I smile at Inda and nod. He looks a little concerned. 'Don't worry darling, we'll be back before you even notice we're gone. Besides, you'll be busy at your singing lesson with Finny,' I assure him.

I feel so much more relaxed now. What a night it's going to be. I'll be a heroine – I'll save my Hamish the Handsome and tell him how to get to my place. Then I'll be able to see him all the time. We can hide him somewhere at home and we'll share our food with him (well, sometimes maybe) and, who knows, maybe Darling and Hayoo might adopt him too.

I'm so lucky to have met so many nice and helpful feelis in here, particularly Raffles and Big Dan who are going to risk their lives to help me tonight. It's really comforting, coz I mean it really *is* hard to get good help these days.

'You know, you three should be getting your nails sharpened in readiness for this escapade tonight,' Zsa Zsa suggests. 'You can get them really sharp by clawing the carpet like this.' I hear a scratching noise, so obviously she's demonstrating. 'Oh darn, I've broken another nail.'

'You surely can't have any left by now,' I say with a smirk.

'Huh?'

It's still nearly three hours until dark so I guess I've just got to sit here and bite my time. Meanwhile, all I've got to look forward to is dinner. I wish Miss Steph would hurry up.

Huh! She must've heard me. Think and ye shall be heard, they say; somebody says. Actually I don't know who says it, but there is Miss Steph, walking in the door with the dinner trolley, just as I'm thinking about her. It must be mental feelipathy! Ooh, or have I discovered the art of hyla?

The Three Amigos

I'm starting to get flupperties in my belly and Inda is a bucket of nerves. It's the waiting that's the worst thing. And the anticipation. And the unknown. And the fear and trepidation and terror and…

'Hey, calm down, Umbi. You look like you're trying to tap dance, or rap dance, and trust me, it's not something you'd want to be seen doing in public.'

'I know darling, but it's not very often I have to crawl out of my comfort zone and contemplate a foray into Weeras in the middle of the night.'

'Well, you don't have to go, you know. I mean–'

'I *do* have to go Inda-mine. I just couldn't live with myself if something bad happened to Hamish the Handsome. If you get to meet him, you'll understand. Some feelis are simply worth fighting for. Many I couldn't give a flick of my tail for, but some, well, I just have to do what I've got to do. His life might depend on it. I might be the only feeli on earth who can save him.'

Inda shrugs in resignation. 'But Umbi, what if something happens to you?'

'Nothing's going to happen to me. I'll have Big Dan and Raffles there to look after me.'

'Speaking of your cohorts in crime,' Big Dan says, as he suddenly appears at our gate like an apparition, 'we're just going to get on the intercat again to figure out the best way to get to the AFAQS. It might be quicker to go cross country, as the Aark-aark flies, rather than sticking to the roads. That way, nobody will notice us either.'

Raffles darts ahead of him through the door into the office. Honestly, I don't know where that kisskie gets all his energy from. He's like a coiled string – always ready to go off.

Inda starts to hum something unrecognisable. I suddenly remember his date, er, singing lesson with the lovely Finny. That's good, maybe she can take his mind off what I'm getting up to.

Raffles appears again and springs up to open the latch on our gate. 'Okay, we've just worked out how to get there and we've calculated that, so long as we don't feelifoot around, it should take us about 45 minutes. So, are you ready? I've just unsnibbed the kitchen door, so we're set to go.'

'Ohh,' I look umbingly at Inda and dop him on the head. 'Here goes then. Now, why don't you trot down to Finny and get started with this singing business. I'll look forward to hearing you when I get back. There's a good dossie.'

He scampers off towards Finny's pen, glancing back at me as he skids to a stop in a grey fuzz.

I follow Big Dan towards the kitchen, where Raffles is darting around and up and down, checking out the shelves and cupboards.

'What are you doing?' I ask him.

'I just figured we might need some escape gear, like a rope or a hacksaw,' he replies, as if I should have figured that out for myself.

'But how are you going to carry it?' I'm betting he hadn't thought of that.

'Do you think I hadn't thought of that?'

'Well–'

'On that,' he points to a plastic tray thingy, 'I'm going to make a harness and tie it to that handle so we can pull it along behind us. Sort of like a tomboggan.'

'A tomboggan.'

'Yes, a tomboggan. Actually Big Dan has offered to pull it, seeing that he's the biggest and strongest.'

I nod. Thank goodness for that. I never was much into winter sports.

We seem to be making good headway and so far it's been an interesting excursion. Fortunately, it's a bright starry night so the visibility is good, not that we feelis have any difficulty seeing in the dark as a rule. But, when you've got to think about navigating, modus operandi, avoiding getting your paws wet and the occasional exercise-induced hunger pangs, you need all the help you can get.

I admit, though, I am starting to wish Raffles and Big Dan would stick to the streets. I think Big Dan's finding the tomboggan a bit awkward, but he's too much of a gentletom to complain.

I've already lost count of how many fences we've climbed or gone under or around or through. I'm not sure Raffles realised there'd be such a bobsical course when he plotted our route. So much for the flying Aark-aark approach.

Fortunately for me the fences haven't been too high coz, as you can imagine, scaling six-footers is not my forte. And I truly hope my two amigos really do know where we're going, because I certainly don't recognise anything in this neighbourwood.

Just as I'm thinking that, my nostrils detect a familiar smell. Quiffo food!

I can spot *that* from a mile away. It smells

just like the stuff our neighbours put out for their obnoxious, snuffling, snorting, snapdragon-excuse for a quiffo. The only good thing about him is that he often doesn't eat all his dinner at once, so I'm more than happy to polish off the rest and lick his plate clean for him.

All I have to do is wait until his deuxjambs call him inside, so I don't have to contend with his whiny voice and bad breath, or worry that he might alert them to my midnight feasting.

I get to thinking about food and lick my lips.

'Hey, guys, do you mind if we take a breather – and a detour?'

'What for? A detour where?' Big Dan asks. 'Just remember, we're doing this for you. And for a feeli we've never even met.'

'Yes, but–'

Big Dan sniffs the air. 'Hmm, I know what you're on about. Do you think we can't smell that too?'

'Well, we need some sustenance. We've still got a big night ahead of us.'

'Why not,' Raffles pipes up. 'I'm a bit peckish myself.'

We veer to the right and sniff along the bottom of a wooden fence.

'It's right there,' I point, 'just on the other side of the fe–'

Before I've even finished the word, Raffles has scaled the palings and is perched on the top. Darn it, this one *is* a six-footer. I look up at the Everest of backyard fortress ramparts. It's daunting. I'm not sure I can get over that, at least not without a substantial run-up and leg-up.

'Psst. Hey, Big Dan, can you just stand right there, so I can use you as a springboard?'

He shakes his head in resignation and slips out of the tomboggan harness. 'Okay, but you'll need to start back there and get some speed up to give yourself some impetus, and please, think light will you?'

'Ha ha.'

'Come on guys,' Raffles whispers, 'we haven't got all night'.

I back up a few metres and drop into pounce mode, wriggling my ooti at the correct speed to give me enough pace for launch mode. 'Are you set, Big Dan?'

He positions himself about a metre away from the fence, stands as tall as he can and braces himself. 'I'll count you down. Ready?'

'Yep.' I wriggle my ooti again in readiness. I'm like a leopard, getting ready to pounce on a jungle creature that smells like dinner. I'm all muscle and concentration; a gymnast preparing to launch at a vault and do some spectacular triple somersault with a twist.

'Three, two, ONE!'

'Huh? Oh.'

I take a run-up and leap, sights set on the top of the fence. I launch off Big Dan's back and fly upwards, bracing myself for impact.

Oops, whoops!

Suddenly my nose is planted in timber. I look heavenwards into Raffles' desperate face. There's nothing the kid can do to help me. I grapple and unsheathe my claws and dig them into the fence. My paws are too far apart and I'm getting splinters in my chin as I start to slide.

This wasn't how I pictured it. I cringe at this ignominious ending to my gymnastic career and slide a bit more. Then I just let go, defeated, and fall backwards onto Big Dan.

'Haha,' Raffles titters.

'Oh, you shut up,' I spit.

'No, you shut up,' he retorts.

'No, *you* shut up,' I re-retort.

'No, I mean, shut up,' he whispers, his paw up to his mouth, 'someone's coming'.

There's a door sliding noise, followed by a deep-voiced deuxjamb yelling, 'Who's there?'

And then comes the craziness.

A demented quiffo, bark-bark-barking like

159

there's no tomorrow, throws his silly self at the fence like he can mush right through it.

'Get it, Titan,' the he-deuxjamb yells.

We have all frozen. Raffles is so stock-still on top of the fence he looks like a stone statue.

Titan?

I'm imaging a German sheepherder or a Bogeyman Pincher or some such huge, slavering, beastly quiffo.

Raffles is completely dumbstruck. His eyes dilate and I swear that, even in the dark, I can see him turning pale.

But, before I can even open my mouth, Big Dan pushes me off and in one amazing, acrocatic manoeuvre, he launches himself to the top of the fence, grabs Raffles in his teeth and lands beside me again.

Raffles is stunned; his dinner-plate eyes are rolling around in his head like it's a turmble-dryer.

'Phew, thanks Big Dan,' Raffles says, barely audible over the snuffling, snarling and growling behind the fence. 'I thought I was a goner. I thought that beast was going to pluck me off the fence and eat me for dessert.'

I can still see the terror in Raffles' eyes. I reckon he's had at least one of his lives scared out of him.

'Well guys,' I say when the other two seem recovered enough, 'I think maybe we'll forget the midnight feast and get cracking. What do you think?'

'Absolutely,' they say in unison.

We skirt along the bottom of the fence until we reach a footpath and then turn right, so that we're now in front of the house with the Bogeyman Pincher; who, by the way, is still barking ferociously.

I peer across the gardening to the see-through fence where Titan has renewed his cacophonous vigil. But something's odd. I take a few paces closer, peering at the salivating quiffo, and then a few more steps... until I'm eye-level with him.

Hang on – eye level?

I can't help it, I really can't... I crack up laughing and turn to Raffles. 'Oh yeah, Raffles, such a big vicious Bogeyman.'

'Ha, ha. That's a Sheet-zoo,' Big Dan says.

'It sure does,' Raffles agrees.

'Huh?' Big Dan and I say at the same time. He cocks his head at me in perplexity. Then he laughs as the penny drops.

'No, Raffles, that's what it *is* – not what it *does,*' he says with a smirk.

I'm lost, because I thought he was talking about a crumby animal-farm; maybe one with no actual animals, or something.

I turn back to the prissy-white yappy quiffo.

'So who's a big ferocious quiffo then?' I tease it, in a kisskie-like catronising voice. 'And who's got pretty pink bows in his hair?'

The quiffo's mouth slaps shut and it backs off, tail between its little legs.

'And that, dear Raffles,' I bat my paws together in the universal signal of job done and dusted, 'is how you dispatch obnoxious, toothy-jowled, slobberholic quiffos'.

I flick my tail pointedly and casually turn and head back towards the footpath giving Big Dan and Raffles a 'come on' with my head. They must be impressed with my quiffo-dispatching bravery as they fall in behind me.

And there we go, walking along the footpath, and I'm feeling pretty pleased with my own bravado, when suddenly my fur starts to frickle uncontrollably, my nose goes all flarey, and my ears involuntarily rotate 360 degrees.

This is Feeli-alert for: *danger, big danger*.

What the? Uh oh. DANGER!

'Run, guys, run!' I say.

I turn my head in time to see three quiffos – Titan has cohorts! – launching themselves out their front door.

'Gaw, get 'em, boys; sick-em,' the evil he-deuxjamb yells.

We run like cut feelis. I'm embarrassed to say I'm struggling because of my flabby-flanks, but Big Dan is right behind me.

Titan is right behind Big Dan; and another one – this one has purple bows – is hot on Raffles' heels, snapping the air.

'Go Titan, go Goliath, go Gigantor,' evil-deuxjamb yells.

Honestly, if I had time and my life didn't depend on me running as fast as I can, I'd laugh out loud. I mean, I've heard of Small Quiffo Syndrome, but this is ridiculous. Titan, Goliath, Gigantor, huh? I'd have called them Itzy, Bitzy and Ditzy myself, but then–

Holy kackapod, they're gaining on us.

And when quiffos are after you it doesn't matter what size they are.

'Run, Juno, run. You too, Raffles.' It's Big Dan of course.

I haven't got the breath to tell him I'm already running as fast as I can.

Just as he's almost alongside me, he suddenly disappears – up a tree.

Why didn't I think of that?

One of the quiffos – I think it's the original Titan – comes to a screeching halt and starts madly berdonking the bottom of the tree.

Just then, Raffles darts past me and suddenly veers off across the road. I see him land on a car roof in a single bound.

Mr Purple Bows, who was right behind him, has nowhere to go and crashes into the side of the car.

Meanwhile, I'm still looking for something scaleable, but I'm fast running out of footpath. Then I spot it.

I dart off to the right, across someone's gardening, springboard off a low thick hedge – wonder for a moment why it's shaped like a giant woozel – and fly like a launching Terrorcacktil onto the top of a fence.

Now why couldn't I do that before?

How I manage not to go straight over the other side is beyond me, but hey, I'm up here and Mr Lavender Bows can suffer in his chokeystrap! He almost falls over himself as he skids to a halt, and yap-yappy-yaps at me with his little fangs bared.

Thank goodness I can catch my breath. From my vantage point, I can see Raffles still perched on top of the car, and although I can't see him, I'm guessing Big Dan is still up his gum tree since Mr Pink Bows is still below barking up a storm.

Phew! I hadn't bargained on this much excitement – or exercise. I sure hope Hamish the Handsome appreciates all this.

The Pawshank Redemption

'It's not far now,' Raffles announces as we approach a treeful area along the edge of a gully.

I'm so glad that evil deuxjamb finally called off his quiffo-hounds and let us get on with our mission. We lost valuable time waiting alone on our perches until they'd gone. And then, of course, the boys had to repair the harness on the tomboggan.

'We've just got to cross over here and head that way a bit and we should see the AFAQS building. I'll lead the way now, if you like,' Raffles announces.

'Sure, lead on,' I say. But no sooner have I said it than Big Dan suddenly rushes forward and dive-bombs onto Raffles, stopping him in his tracks.

'What the hell's that all about?' Raffles asks as he gets up and dusts himself off. 'If you wanted to go first, why didn't you just say so, ooh, what's that? That sticky, it's moo-oo-oving.'

'That's why I stopped you silly. Coz that's no sticky – it's a creely!'

'Oh cripes, a creely?'

'Yes, and a dangerous one too. One bite from that and you'd be deader that a dead dongo's dinger,' Big Dan explains as the stripy mobile-sticky slinkers away.

'I got bitten by one once. My own foolish fault really since I thought it looked tasty. But it turns out it was more interested in eating *me*. By-Basht, I was crook. Never been so sick. I thought I was off to Weeras for sure. Thankfully my deuxjambs found me in time. I spent a week in the hostipple with all sorts of tubes sticking in and out of me. Not a pretty sight. And it took me quite a while to get over it.'

I'm so impressed by Big Dan's bravery I tell him so. 'Oh, you're so brave, Big Dan. Fancy, neither of us would have known what it was until we stepped on it – and then it might have been too late. Cripes. I'm so glad you're with us.'

Without realising it, I start to quirrel and I dop my head under Big Dan's chin and rub my shoulder up against his.

'I'm glad I'm with you too, Juno,' he says, in his mesmeriso voice. 'I can't imagine what fate might have befallen you if I'd left you and Raffles to your own devices.'

I go all gooey. I think I'd go to the ends of the earth if Big Dan were by my side. But then, I'd do that for Hamish too – I remind myself.

We head across the gully, shoulder to shoulder, with Raffles skipping along beside us. As we get to the crest at the other side, Raffles points over to the left.

'That's it. That building over there, with the cyclone fence around it,' he says animatedly.

I can't help wondering how a fence like that could keep a cyclone out, but then a lot of things deuxjambs do leave me scratching my ooti. It's a very solid-looking brick building though, but even it doesn't look impenetrable. As we get closer though, I'm not so sure.

'Geez,' Raffles says, 'that looks more daunting than Pawshank Prison. Can you see any windows or some other way in?'

'We'll have to get a bit closer,' Big Dan says.

I nod in agreement. 'Just remember guys, this place is designed to keep quiffos in, as well as feelis.'

'You mean there's quiffos in there?' Raffles asks, with more than a skerrick of concern in his voice.

'Of course, d'oh,' I say.

'Oh cripes. I think I must have temporarily blocked that knowledge from my thoughts,' Raffles says.

'Okay, Mister Escapologist, Mister Houdini, so how are we going to get in here?' Big Dan asks.

'Hey, give me a break will you. I'm used to breaking *out* of places – I've never actually broken *into* one.'

'You picked your time to tell us that,' I comment.

'Well give me a minute. We'll have to case the place – right around – to find its most vulnerable spot.'

'Sounds reasonable,' says Big Dan as we patrol along the outside of the wire fence.

Before long we come to some shrubbery and the fence does a sharp left turn. We pick our way under some prickly bushes and emerge into a car park. There's a lot of concrete, but no cars, which means – phew – there's no deuxjambs either.

We saunter along in front of the building like we're out for a Sunday constitutional, until we come to a glass door and window. We peer in but can't make out anything very interesting. Raffles looks at me and shrugs. Suddenly he launches off his haunches and grabs the door lever. It doesn't budge. Of course. I mean, we didn't really expect it to.

'Worth a try, I guess,' I whisper to him.

We keep going across the front of the building, turn around the corner and come to a fence; fortunately one designed to keep quiffos in, not feelis out. I take the lead and poke my head and shoulders through. Foop. I'm stuck.

Raffles scampers through the gap beside me and grabs my chokeystrap in his mouth and starts to pull. I'm not going anywhere.

167

'Here, give us a paw Big Dan,' Raffles says.

'Breathe in, honey, I'll give you a push from the back. Don't mind my paws there.'

'I don't mind your paws at all,' I say suggestively. 'Call me honey again and I'll do anything, Big Dan.'

'All right then, but for now, just breathe in when I push, okay?'

I do as he says and after some pretty heavy breathing and intermittent exhaling, not to mention a few grunts, the rest of me is squeezed through the fence. Big Dan tilts his huge head sideways, pushes it through the bars and then elongates his body and slides through.

'Okay,' says Raffles, 'let's see what's down here.'

We sneak along the edge of the building and I realise the most surprising thing is how quiet it is. I would have thought that homeless quiffos would be howling all night. I wonder where the feeli quarters are; hopefully we don't need to go anywhere near the quiffos to get to them.

We get to the end of the building without even passing any doors. There are some high windows, but they look a bit tricky and unlikely as an access point. We turn left again and there, in the end of the building, is a wire gate.

'Ah-ha!' Raffles exclaims.

'Shh,' Big Dan and I say together.

'This looks promising,' Raffles whispers. 'Look, this is the quiffos' quarters. Look at all the gates in there and–

'Uh-oh, quiffos.'

That explains the snoring and grunting I can hear. But I'm dumbfounded that none of them has heard us yet, I mean it's not like we've done SAS training. There's no way we're gonna go through there to find Hamish. I shake my head at the other two and point around the corner.

Raffles motions to us to stay put and takes off around the last bend to check things out. A few moments later he's back again.

'Nup, no way in around there, just a solid door. This is the only way.'

'But we can't get through that,' I say, stating the obvious.

'You two can't maybe, but I can,' he whispers. 'After all, you *are* looking at the Copacatbana Club's two-time limbo champion.'

Big Dan raises his eyebrows. 'Really,' he says in a deep, unconvinced voice.

'Really?' I ask.

'Really,' he says. 'Look, I'll show you.'

With that, he turns around, flops onto his back and flattens himself out like a ribbon. Then, and I can't explain how, he glides backwards and gets his chin under the gate, then his front paws and he wriggles his way through to the other side. I wouldn't have believed it if I didn't just see it for myself. Incredible.

'That's incredible,' I whisper and Big Dan nods in agreement. 'Now what are you going to do?'

He mooshes and gestures: 'I'll go through and open the front door. You two go back around and I'll let you in.'

Sounds feasible. Big Dan and I nod at each other. But we wait a bit to watch Raffles' progress through the gauntlet of quiffos. He tiptoes along looking cautiously from side to side. Considering our earlier episode with Sheet-zoos I can't believe how brave he is.

I also can't believe how quiet he is and how none of the quiffos can hear him. He's silently putting one paw in front of the other.

I think of all those fighty-films, with the writing on the bottom, that Hayoo watches where a warrior always goes slinky-like-a-feeli through a building and then something goes 'clang' and everyone wakes up and runs around and turns all the lights on and there's fighting.

Now, here *we* are watching Raffles go all tippy like a deuxjamb-Ninja; and I cross my claws for him. I also squint and cringe a bit, as though that's going to help.

He gets to the far end of the space and turns to us and points off to the right then heads in that direction. There's not a peep from any of the quiffos.

As Big Dan and I get around the front of the building again, after another squishy shimmy though the fence, Raffles is sitting on the door mat nonchalantly licking his paws, the front door open behind him. I'm starting to believe his Houdini claim. He looks up at us.

'What took you so long?'

'Well done, kid,' I say as I put my paw up to give him five.

The flupperties are really causing a commotion in my stomach now as we cross the threshold into the AFAQS. I'm coming Hamish, I think to myself.

'I think the feelis must be this way,' Raffles points to a door off to the right. 'I didn't pass any coming through there.'

Big Dan goes ahead and pushes at the door which opens smoothly into a hallway. We follow him through and before long we emerge into a bigger room. This one has gates all the way around and I count about half a dozen snoozing feelis. It's not nearly as bad as I thought it would be, but not nearly as good or as comfortable as the Lap of Luxury.

As we pass one of the pens, a nondescript beige feeli puts its head up, yawns and stretches. Then it spots us. It looks pretty astonished.

'Hey, watcha doing out there?' it asks.

'Huh? Oh just looking for someone,' I reply.

'Oh. Who?'

'Hamish. Hamish the Handsome.'

'Nup, don't know 'im. Don't think he's in here.'

'No, apparently he's in Weeras Way. Do you know where that is?'

'Oh no, you don't want to go there – not voluntarily.'

'But we have to. We're here to rescue him.'

'Oh,' beige feeli answers as though this is an everyday occurrence. 'In that case, it's through that door over there.' He points to the other end of the room.

'Hey,' says Raffles suddenly. 'Do you want me to let you out of there?'

'Let me out? Why?'

'Because I can and maybe there's somewhere else you'd rather be.'

'No, not particularly.'

'Okay, your call,' Raffles says.

We head towards the door to Weeras Way, not knowing what to expect on the other side. Usually whenever someone goes to Weeras, you never see them again.

But then Inda is living proof that Weeras isn't necessarily always bad. After all, I never thought I'd see *him* again when he was taken away. Raffles leaps up to flick the door lever and Big Dan pushes it open.

When we get inside we see three small cages up on a bench. I look up at the first one – it's empty. No Hamish. I'm not sure whether that's good or bad.

The second one looks like it's occupied but all I can see is a lank-looking tail hanging over the edge of a cushiony thing. I'm pretty sure that's not Hamish either.

There's a little sign on the outside of the cage, but I can't figure out what it means. It says:

Case #2339
DSH/F
Entry 22/12
Vet/euth 16/02

'Hey, guys, what do you think the note on this cage means?'

Big Dan and Raffles peer at the card.

'Well, I think the case number and the entry

date are pretty obvious,' Big Dan says. 'And DSH, I believe, means domestic short-hair, F is obviously female. As for vet/ euth 16/02...

'Uh-oh, I have this awful feeling–'

'What?'

'I'm pretty sure this means that this girl is going all the way to Weeras tomorrow.'

Raffles eyes go all huge. 'You mean–'

'Yep.'

'Oh no.' Now I'm panicky. I scan the tag on the next cage.

Case # 2377
DLH/M
Entry 14/01
Vet/euth 16/02

As I fling myself up onto the counter beside the cage, a matted grey head untucks itself from a tangled mass of fur and slowly turns towards me. Its eyes aren't focused yet but I'd know them anywhere.

'Hamish, Hamish. I'm here!'

He looks pretty astonished, I must say. Actually perplexed more than astonished. And although I hate to say it, he's not as handsome as I remember. In fact he looks like he's been through a haystack backwards – a muddy, stinky haystack. He's definitely on the nose.

'Is that you, Juno? What are you doing here?' he asks sleepily.

'I've – that is, we've – come to rescue you.' I put my paw through the wire and touch him on the head.

'Rescue? But how did you know I was here? And how did you get here?'

'No time to explain. C'mon we're gonna get you out of here. My friends Big Dan and Raffles have come to help me get you out.'

'Thank goodness. I was getting pretty bored in here.'

'Bored is the least of your worries, Hamish. You're gonna be a goner tomorrow, if we don't get you out of here.'

'A goner? What do you mean?'

'I mean curtains, finito, the Weeras of no return.'

'Awps! Are you kidding? You mean...' he runs his paw across his throat.

'Yep.'

'Who's there? What did you wake me up for?' a sleepy but irritated voice from the other cage says.

'Hi,' says Raffles, 'we're the rescue committee. We've come to bust you out of here. I'm Raffles – AKA Houdini.'

'Huh? Oh, hi, I'm Jorjie. Boy, are you a funny looking thing.'

'Yeah, well you're no oil painting either,' Raffles says to the little teezee.

'We're gonna rescue your neighbour here, too,' I say to Hamish, 'whether she likes it or not'.

With that, Raffles flicks the catch on Jorjie's cage and then cuts across to open Hamish's latch.

He's free! He steps out and dops my head with his. He's a bit stinky, but we'll worry about that later.

The break-out was so much easier than I thought it would be. We didn't even need any of the gear on the tomboggan, let alone the tomboggan itself, so we leave it behind in the car park.

Despite their initial reaction to each other upon meeting, Raffles now seems to be quite taken with Jorjie – the two have skipped on ahead of us. Hamish, Big Dan and I are strolling all casual, since the break-out didn't take as long as we'd anticipated. We retrace our steps back to the Lap of Luxury.

Big Dan and I have just been telling Hamish about our episode with the three snappy quiffos.

He seemed to think it was funnier than we did. But now I come to think of it, it was pretty funny, I guess, and it will add to the excitement when we tell everyone about our adventure.

'I can't thank you enough for this,' Hamish says, rubbing himself against my flank.

'Well, I reckon you'd have done the same for me if the circumstances had been reversed.'

'I would indeed,' he says.

'One thing I want to know though, is why you're so – um, shall we say – unkempt.'

'Well, it's like this – and don't you dare laugh. I was outside one night a few months back and it was absolutely frigid, I reckon about minus twenty or so. Anyway, I was thirsty, and I could see water on the metal of my deuxjambs' shed, so I stuck my tongue out to lick it and… and it stuck. I couldn't let go. There I was, standing there, freezing to death, my fur turning into icicles, my paws like ice cubes and my tongue stuck fast to the stupid wall.'

I tried really hard not to titter at this mental image. Hamish would be mortified if I laughed at him. 'So how long were you there like that?'

'Until morning, I think about four or five hours. Fortunately, by then my tongue was so numb I couldn't feel it.'

I shivered. 'Ooh, you poor thing. So what happened then?'

'Finally, the sun came out, just enough to melt the ice so I could pull my tongue off.'

'Errgh.' I shuddered.

'Unfortunately, I think I left behind the brushes on my tongue, see,' he pokes his tongue out at me and it looks quite gruesomely black and completely devoid of bristles, 'which means not only can I not taste anything anymore, I also can't groom myself properly. My tongue just slides off. That explains why my fur looks so bad.'

'But it doesn't explain how you ended up in AFAQS. Didn't

your deuxjambs come for you? I remember you telling me your deuxjambs were really nice.'

'Ah, but of course, you couldn't know that I have – er, had – new deuxjambs since we last saw each other and they didn't treat me the same as the old ones. I got picked up one night when I was just minding my own business in a rubbish bin, and brought here. The new deuxjambs never came to look for me and nobody else wanted me either; especially not when I look like this. I've been at the AFAQS for ages.'

'Well, don't you worry. We're going to take you back with us to the Lap of Luxury, where I'm gonna spend the rest of the night getting you cleaned up. Then, I'm sure Miss Steph will look after you.'

'I don't know what you're talking about, Juno, but it sounds mighty good to me,' my hunk of a Hamish says.

Flanked by Big Dan *and* Hamish the Handsome as we make our way back, I feel so safe and secure – sort of like the Vegemice in a sandwich, except *I'm* not going to get eaten.

I can't believe how happy I am.

I grin like a Cheshire Feeli.

From here to caternity

'Aaah… ooh,' I yawn. The sun's about to come up by the look of it. That's something you don't see every day. It's been quite a night, so it's no surprise that I can barely keep my eyes open. And my tongue is literally aching.

We got back here at about 3.30am and since then, I kid you not, I've been licking Hamish all over to try to get him cleaned up. I haven't had a wink of sleep.

He tasted pretty disgusting I hate to say, and his ears were, well *urgh, blah, pth pth*. I still can't get that taste out of my mouth. But I'm not complaining, really I'm not. Because he was enjoying every minute of it, judging by his deafening quirrelling. I was quirrelling a bit myself, between mouthfuls of dirt and grime.

He's still pretty matted – I mean it would take me three days to get right through his coat, but he's looking a whole lot better now than he did last night.

He's right here beside me on the shelf, napping contentedly and probably dreaming about all the lives he still has left – thanks to moi.

By the time we got back, it was a bit late to introduce him to everybody as we were all pretty bushed. Big Dan and Raffles just fell into bed. Well, Raffles did *after* he spent at least half an hour saying goodbye to Jorjie and telling her he'd look her up when he gets out of here. I'm not sure he really will, because she was really too old for him and goodness knows where she'll end up. But at least she won't be going to terminal Weeras tomorrow.

When we got back inside, Inda was sleeping so peacefully I didn't have the heart to wake him.

So I'm sitting here now pondering what to do about Hamish. Do I wake him up now and send him off out the door, like we planned last night, with directions to my place so he can hang around there for a couple of days until I get home?

Do I just leave him where he is for Miss Steph to find? What will she do? Will she take him straight back to AFAQs? Will she take care of him herself? Will she kick him out the door? I just don't know.

I wish I could stay with him forever though. I can imagine there'd be plenty of times when we could just cuddle up beside each other and sleep the day away or go out exploring and enjoy adventures together. We could even go out on the town at night occasionally, which is something I definitely don't get to do very often.

Of course I'd love to be able to do all of that with Big Dan too, but I keep forgetting that he has his own home to go to and deuxjambs who love him. But I think I'd really enjoy licking inside his ears and all those awkward spots he can't get to himself. Hmmph. I can't believe I'm feeling so domesticated – next I'll be wanting to help Hayoo with the sucker-dragon.

It's nice though, to have this quiet time to ponder to myself. Maybe I should think about waking up early occasionally – it's amazing how sharp the mind can be at this hour. Only drawback is, you've just got to wait longer for breakfast. So what's the point?

Maybe I'll just close my eyes for a bit and then I'll wake

Hamish up before Miss Steph's due to arrive so we can plan what we're going to do. Oh I'm full of good ideas...zzz

I nearly jump out of my skin as I feel a definite-deuxjamb hand stroking my flank. Oh cripes, I've slept in again. Before I even open my eyes, the panic starts to set in: Hamish, what about Hamish? I didn't wake up – to wake *him* up. Talk about sprung!

'Hello Miss Fudgepuddle – who's a sleepyhead?' It's Miss Steph of course. 'And hello young man; my gosh, you're as lazy as your mother.'

I hear Inda yawn and, as I peer over the shelf – I've got the top bunk – he's stretching his legs out and splaying his toes. But where's Hamish? I mean, he was right here beside me before. Surely Miss Steph must have seen him.

'Hamish!' I call out, trying not to sound too panicky.

'It's all right,' Big Dan calls back, 'he's hiding'.

'Hiding where?'

'He's in here with me.'

'But that's no good. She'll find him when she gets there.'

'No, she won't.'

'How come?'

'Because he's an expert at feelichatra.'

'You're kidding me. Well I never; but how – uh, where?'

'Right at the moment, he looks exactly like the grey blanket in my cushy-house. She'll never even see him in there, he's so well catouflaged.'

'Huh? You mean – that's the secret? Catouflage? Just blend with your surroundings?'

'Yep,' Hamish replies in a muffled voice. 'That's it – feelichatra in a nutshell. Of course some of us find it easier than others and it's definitely an advantage being grey, or teezee, maybe. I mean, if I'm out in the garden – my deuxjambs can never find me because I just blend with the scenery. I can look like a shadow, a tree, the grass, the side of a building. It's a bit harder if I'm inside although I *can* disappear into the bedroom carpet sometimes.

'You, on the other hand, would always find it difficult because – well, white and orange don't blend with so many things.'

'I'm not *orange*, I'm ginger.'

'Call it what you want – you *look* orange.'

'Oh. Yuck! I hate orange – it clashes with *everything*!'

Zsa Zsa suddenly pipes up. 'It also doesn't help that you're – er, so flabby. That makes it more difficult to vanish. You should look up your jes, what's her name? – when you get out of here; she's supposedly the expert at feelichatra isn't she?'

'You mean Sizi? Yes, Zsa Zsa – I will look her up. That's another thing on my list of things to do when I get out of here. I'm sure Inda will be able to help me with Hayoo's puterbox at home. There's all sorts of things I'd like to look up – at my leisure.

'I'd like to look up that Scottish guy with the nose, too, to find out a bit more about my ancestry. He might also have some ideas about how I could get to Americat for the convention. What's his name again?'

'You mean Jock?' the Colonel asks.

'Yeah. So how do I contact him? Has he got a weblike?'

'Think so. It's something like www.noseabout.tom.'

'Noseabout?'

'Maybe it's nosearound, or nose into,' the Colonel ponders aloud. 'You know, something to do with his nose'.

'No nose is good nose?' Choux-Fleur suggests.

'Brown-nose maybe,' says Finny.

'Follow your nose,' says Humbug.

'Poke your nose into,' Maharani offers.

'I know, I know,' Raffles buts in, 'nose to the ground; no, nose to the grindstone.'

'Ouch,' Zsa Zsa comments, 'that would hurt'.

'No skin off my nose,' Raffles laughs.

'Oh, now you're just getting silly,' Zsa Zsa says.

'Don't look down your nose at me,' Raffles retorts. 'Ha, ha, and don't stick it in the air either.'

This whole conversation is just going around in circles. 'I'm sorry I asked,' I say, a little put out.

'Well don't get your nose out of joint or you might need a nose job,' Big Dan laughs, then immediately apologises. 'Oh sorry, Juno, I couldn't resist. But be careful when you find him, coz you'll pay through the nose for his services, ha-ha.' He falls over laughing. 'I mean, you don't want to cut off your nose to spite your face.'

'Oh for goodness sake, I really *am* sorry I asked.' I'm no better off than when I started this conversation.

'Thenoseknows,' the Colonel suddenly blurts, 'I knew I'd remember it eventually. That's it www.thenoseknows.tom.'

'Hmm – you'll remember that, won't you Inda?'

'Yep, for sure,' he replies.

Miss Steph interrupts our conversation. 'What are you chatting about there?'

'If you only knew,' I say as I roll into a demi-ipwod.

She scratches me under the chin, just where I like it and I endow her with a quirrel. I suppose I can't hold it against her that she destroyed my tricerapots, I mean, she's just a deuxjamb after all.

Hayoo and Darling are much more on the ball. I'm sure *they'll* be impressed when I show them what I can do. Maybe *they'll* contact *Sixty Mittens* and then I'll be famous. Hey, Hayoo has all that paper in her office; just think about what I'll be able to do with that. I could decorate the whole house with origami art. Mmm, you know, as much as I'm enjoying my holiday here, I sort of wish I could hurry up and get home. There's so much stuff to get on with.

Miss Steph pours some much-anticipated kitzbitz into our bowls and backs out of our quarters.

'Hey Umbi,' Inda snaps me from my reverie. 'Finny thinks I have a good voice. She wants to teach me some more.'

'Is that so, Finny?' I call out.

'Oh yes, Fudg– Sorry, Juno. He's quite a natural. We had a great time while you were off on your rescue mission last night, didn't we everyone?'

She's almost drowned out by a chorus of agreeable comments.

'He'll do very well under Finny's tutelage,' the Colonel says. 'Even the best singers need extra coaching'.

'We all think he should go on The FeeliX Factor or maybe The Miaow,' Maharani says. 'He's a better singer than anyone else here. Oh, except for Finny, that is'.

'He sang quite a repertoire,' Zsa Zsa reports, 'from old stuff like Elton Upjohn's *Honky Feeli* and Poison's *Look What the Feeli Dragged In* to stuff from musicals like *Caturday Night Fever, Ocathoma* and *The Sound of Caterwauling*. I know all the songs from that because my umbi was in a production of it along with a few other musicals like *Crease, My Fair Feeli* and *Umbi Mia.'*

'My favourite,' Humbug interrupts, 'was that *If I Were a Rich Cat* from *Fiddler on a Hot Tin Roof.* Inda really sang that well. Very entertaining.'

Big Dan sniggers. 'I think you'll find that's *Fiddler on the Roof,* Humbug, not to be confused with the movie *Feeli on a Hot Tin Roof'*.

'Oh yes, I *knew* that Big Dan. I was just, um–'

'Confused?'

'Mm.'

I'd be doing well if I had the vaguest idea what they were all talking about. I make a mental pact with myself to learn more about this from Inda when we get home.

Musicals have never really been my bowl of yellum, but

then that's probably because I haven't paid much attention to them. I suspect there's a lot that Inda – and all my other kisskies for that matter – could teach me. Maybe I've led too sheltered a life. I'm going to make up for that. I'm going to get out there and strut my stuff. Somehow, I'm going to get to the origami qualifier, but in the meantime, I'm going to spend as much time as I can perfecting my techniques. I'll show the world how clever I am and I'll learn everything about *everything*. Then I won't ever be embarrassed about my shortcomings – coz I won't have any.

I'm also going to find out more about my ancatsry and see if there's any ecsotiques hiding in there. I just know that there's got to be more to me than everyone thinks. I feel it in my bones that I'm not just a plain old ordinary wuzzer.

And I'm going to organise a reunion – get all my precious, clever kisskies together. And, presuming that Hamish is going to be around a bit, I'm going to get him to help me perfect feelichatra. And I'm sure there's other things he could teach me. It's going to be so much fun when we get out of here coz he'll be able to visit and maybe, just maybe, Darling and Hayoo will let him stay. We've got a lot of plans to make, but I can't really talk to him now coz Miss Steph's just about to go into Big Dan's place. I can hear her talking to him.

'Hello there, Fess, you bootiful pooty tat. You're such a honey boy aren't you?'

I'm finding it hard to resist the urge to giggle. I can just picture Big Dan trying to look tough while Miss Steph slavers all over him.

'Today is washing day, my boy,' Miss Steph announces.

'Oh no, no, not the cushy bed thing – no don't touch it. Just stay put Hamish!'

I can hear the panic in Big Dan's voice.

'Uh-oh,' says Hamish. 'I think I'm sprung.'

'But you're an expert at feelichatra,' I call out, trying to contain the panic in my voice.

'She mightn't be able to see me, but she'll sure feel me when she picks– Uh-oh and oops!'

'What on earth?' Miss Steph asks querulously. 'Big Dan what have you got in here? Oh, oh my goodness. Where on earth did you come from?'

'Oh dear.' That's all I can think of to say.

'I think I'm done for,' Hamish says. I can hear the anguish in his voice. 'Please, please don't take me back to the AFAQS,' he begs.

Of course Miss Steph can't understand a word he's saying – he might as well be taking Tonkinese.

Now what's going to happen?

'Hamish, Hamish, don't worry. Everything will be all right. I'm sure it will.' I try to sound really positive, like I know what I'm taking about, but deep down I'm really worried. I can hear Miss Steph approaching. I look out through my wire and there she goes, heading towards the kitchen – with Hamish. She's holding him way out in front of herself by the scruff of the neck, with the other hand under his back legs, and screwing up her nose.

'What a grotty, grotty boy you are. Where on earth did you come from?'

'Nooo,' Hamish yarls as he passes by. 'Help Juno!' His legs are flailing helplessly and the expression on his face just turns my oogies to mush.

'Oh gawd.'

'What do you reckon she's gonna do with him, Juno?' Raffles asks anxiously. 'I hope we didn't go to all that trouble last night for nothing.'

'Me too Raffles, me too. I don't know what to do.'

'I don't know whether there's much we *can* do. But I think we'd better start thinking – and fast,' Raffles says. He sounds as uptight as I feel.

The kitchen door slides shut. My Hamish is on the other side – with Miss Steph!

What's happening? I wish I could see. Arrg, the suspenders is killing me!

My thoughts are suddenly interrupted by Rabbit.

'Incoming, incoming.'

I'm not really interested in that; I'm too busy worrying about my Hamish. What's she doing to him in there? I hear him scream – a blood-curdling yarl.

Is she murdering him?

No, surely not. Get a grip girl. Miss Steph wouldn't do that. She loves us – all of us.

Maybe she's just combing him – or giving him a bath. I focus my ears on the kitchen door but I'm distracted by other noises. I hear a car door slam and now I'm hearing the front door creaking – a voice calls out.

'Hello, hello, Stephanie, are you there? It's Emma Campbell here. We've arrived home early so I was hoping I could collect my Megsy now.'

'Oh foop!'

Fin J. Ross

Fin is a journalist and creative writing tutor who runs a boarding cattery and breeds Bengal and British shorthair cats at her home on the Gippsland Lakes.

She and her husband, Steve, also fabricate cat havens to keep other people's feelis safe and happy.

They enjoy life with their own menagerie: *Selby* the golden retriever; and their domestic cats *Vesper, Moo Moo and Stewie*; their Bengals *Bijou, Reini, Heathcliff, Jolie* and *Nelson*; and their British shorthair *Venus*.

She is also co-author, with her sister, Lindy Cameron, of the true crime anthologies: *Killer in the Family* and *Murder in the Family* (not their own families, of course).

Acknowledgements

Running a boarding cattery and filling my days cuddling, talking to, cleaning up after and generally spending quality time with cats makes me one the luckiest people on earth. But of course, every evening when I've tucked all the happy campers into bed and am locking the door to keep them safe, I always wonder what they get up to when I'm not there.

Some of the things I've imagined is where the idea for *A.K.A. Fudgepuddle* came from.

I also know that cats have an entirely different outlook on life from humans, with their own vocabulary, their own names for themselves and, of course, their own agendas. I tried to put myself into their 'paws' to solve the puzzle of what they get up to when we are not looking and why they behave the way they do.

Some of my regular customers might recognise their own cats as characters in *AKA Fudgepuddle*, while other feelis are combinations of several different cats.

I truly appreciate the lovely deuxjambs who entrust their beloved feelis to my care, just a few of whom, along with their inspirational cats, are mentioned here:

Chris Roep — and the late *Megsy*, who was the inspiration for my Fudgepuddle; Danny & Marg Cusack — Raffles; Bruce & Annie Downing — Fred; Shirley Bowler — Dusty; Karen Day — Billi; Brian & Linda Collins — Professor Willy Pickles; Annabel Davidson — Cobweb; Hilary & Barry Arnold — Romulus & Remus; Richard & Barb Olsen — Megg & the late Figgaro; Di Anderson — Tiffy & Bridgette; Ross & Anne Tucker — Isis & Tut; Laurie & Robyn Bouch — Lulu; Pete & Kim Nicolson — Boo & the late Belle; and Mike & Tanya Ward — Boots, Mao, Chloe & Penny.

A big thank you to Steve who has been my sounding board, chief critic and biggest fan throughout the writing of Fudgepuddle, and who has contributed some wonderful ideas to the storyline.

And a big thank-you to Lindy who believed in this story and wanted to publish it.

Thank you also to the members of my writing class who have put up with me talking about this book for three years.

Thanks to Val and Ian for giving me the wherewithal to write.

Thank you Liz Cameron, my Mum, for a lifetime of opportunities.

Stay tuned for **Fudgepuddle Goes to Hollypudd.**

GENRE FICTION SPECIALISTS

BOOKS & EBOOKS

AN INDEPENDENT AUSTRALIAN PUBLISHING HOUSE

www.clandestinepress.com.au

crime   historical   speculative fiction

science fiction   fantasy   adventure

horror   thriller   urban fantasy

cats

ALSO FROM CLAN DESTINE PRESS

Printed in Australia
Ingram Content Group Australia Pty Ltd
AUHW021431050324
391323AU00001B/1